SPARK – Voices At Play.   2196826

HERTFORDSHIRE COUNTY LIBRARY
COUNTY HALL, HERTFORD.

L.32

There seems, happily for her publishers and her admiring readers, no limit to the manifestations of Muriel Spark's arresting talent. She is certainly one of the most important writers to have emerged in England since the war.

She made her debut as a short-story writer, winning the first prize in the competition organized by the *Observer*. Her novels have had a striking reception on both sides of the Atlantic. Recently she has attracted a great deal of notice with some radio plays specially commissioned by the B.B.C. These, as she presents them, are a new art-form; if a phrase can be invented to describe them, they are dramatic narrations, and interleaved here with stories written to be read, they combine to offer a vivid impression of an unusual talent at work. *Voices at Play* contains four plays and six stories.

VOICES AT PLAY

BY

MURIEL SPARK

LONDON

MACMILLAN & CO LTD

NEW YORK · ST MARTIN'S PRESS

1961

Bbl 11348

MACMILLAN AND COMPANY LIMITED
London Bombay Calcutta Madras Melbourne

THE MACMILLAN COMPANY OF CANADA LIMITED
Toronto

ST MARTIN'S PRESS INC
New York

PRINTED IN GREAT BRITAIN

Author's Note

THIS book contains two different forms of writing: short stories and radio plays. The excuse for both sorts being put together is that all were written on the same creative wavelength. The plays were written for the outward, and the stories for the inward, ear. But one form of writing was very much affected by the other, and so I hope they show a consistent mood.

The plays were written at the suggestion of Mr. Rayner Heppenstall for the Third Programme. By definition they were supposed to be 'features' rather than proper plays. I never quite grasped the distinction between dramatic features and plays except to discern what was in my favour, namely the freedom to do as I pleased with characters and voices without thought of conforming to a settled category. I turned my mind into a wireless set and let the characters play on my ear. Sometimes Mr. Heppenstall clamoured for more visual bits to be written in, so that the listener's imagination could be supplied with what was wanting to the eye.

And so if the plays have turned out to be plays, that is by accident; and if it comes to that, in many ways the same could be said of the stories.

M.S.

v

Contents

The Danger Zone

AN ELEMENTAL DRAMA

CHARACTERS

Richard Jones	a 'bachelor craftsman'
Ruth David	a widow
Simon Rhys	
Margiad Rhys	his wife
John Farmer	
Dr. Evans	
The Rev. Hugh Pugh	

(Young people):
  Mark Farmer
  Lily David
  Freda Rhys
  Jones
  Thomas Pugh
  Connie Evans
  The Danger-Boy

JONES'S DITTY

My girl's gone to skin and bone
Since she went to the Danger-Zone.
My girl-guide
Is my pride
Hiding tidy in the mountain side.

I

My old man's got rolling tight
Swallowing water day and night.
He's got a thirst
To make him burst.
Danger, danger, burning bright.

What's become of my kith and kin?
They grow fat while I grow thin.
Dig the grave
In a wide Welsh cave.
But this is the place where I begin.

1. THE VALLEY

(*Sound of glasses and mineral-water bottles being opened*)

Richard. Speaking as a bachelor craftsman——

Simon. As a bachelor craftsman you've got no right to speak.

Ruth. This is Richard's parlour, Simon.

Simon. But he's got no children, officially. Open a bottle of mineral for Ruth.

Ruth. None the less, it's his parlour that he's given us for the discussion. Thanks, Richard, this is my last. Richard's got a right to speak under his own roof and . . .

John. What were you going to say, then, Richard?

Richard. No, no. It doesn't matter.

Ruth. Now, come on, Richard. Say what you were . . . Come on, Richard.

Richard. No, let it be. Carry on, it's your affair.

John. We aren't getting any further in any case. Open a bottle of the water for Richard, Simon.

Ruth. The children will be wondering where we are.

John. ⎱ They won't think of looking for us at
      Richard's. . . .
Simon. ⎰ . . . won't think of Richard's.

Richard. Ta. It's good stuff.

John. It was better during the war.

Richard. How many's left in the crate?

John. I say we aren't getting any further. Dr. Evans, you've said there's nothing wrong with the young people's eyes. I say there is something wrong.

Ruth. Five — six — *seven* left in the crate.

Dr. Evans. Their eyesight was tested just before they left school.

Richard. . . . and the half-dozen of John's behind the sofa.

Dr. Evans. I can't say if there's anything gone wrong in the last year, can I? I would need to send them in to be tested at the optician's. But if they can see to run around the way they do . . .

Richard. We won't get through all that.

John. We aren't getting any further. There must be something wrong with their eyesight if there's something wrong with the shape of their eyes.

Ruth. My Lily can see all right. She can see too much. She can see what isn't there. (*Silence.*)

John. Yes, like young Mark. If his mother was here she could tell you some stories about Mark since his eyes changed their shape. He stares and stares, and by God when you look to see what he's staring at, it's nothing. What's going to happen when all the other boys in the place turn sixteen? Are they going to turn slit-eyed like Chinamen? We aren't getting any further.

Dr. Evans. There may be something in the atmospherics of this area which affects the shape of the eye.

Ruth. Weren't you born here, Dr. Evans?

Dr. Evans. Yes, oh yes.

Ruth. So was I. And my eyes are round as round. So are my mother's and my uncle's, and my late husband had such big round . . .

Dr. Evans. Ruth, I wouldn't say your eyes were quite round, you know. They are slightly almond shaped like the eyes of all us Celts.

Ruth. My Lily's eyes have gone past the Celtic stage, they're a couple of narrow slits like a bloody cat's.

John. Pass your glass, Ruth . . . Dr. Evans . . .

(*Glass and bottle sounds*)

. . . I'll tell you, Doctor, all the youngsters from the age of sixteen are like foreigners.

Simon. Or criminals. . . .

John. No, foreigners. Mind you, I'm a Yorkshireman myself originally, though I've lived here a long time. But I'm speaking as . . .

Richard. Speaking as a bachelor craftsman, I well recall that my eyes went narrow at sixteen. It was to avoid the chips off the wood, that's what . . .

Simon. Richard, these reminiscences are all very well in their place, but our children aren't bachelor craftsmen. . . .

4

Richard. They're crafty. Ho! Where's your glass, Simon?

Simon. (*Drinking.*) This is a good consignment.

John. During the war it was better. . . .

Ruth. Do you notice the children's voices now? There's a question. Let's face it. That's the question.
   (*All become more excited except Dr. Evans who is rather bored*)

John. They won't open their mouths properly when they speak. That's why we can't make head or tail . . .

Ruth. It's not that at all, John. They speak foreign.

John. They're putting it on. We aren't getting any further.

Simon. Dr. Evans, you should see these boys and girls and judge for yourself. It's no joke. We haven't met here for nothing.

Richard. (*Opens bottle.*) Your glass, John.

Ruth. They speak foreign. They see foreign.

Dr. Evans. English, do you mean?

Simon. No, foreign. The accent. Like Germans, Poles, Czechs, Croats. . . .

John. Russians, Chinese, Laplanders. . . .

Dr. Evans. They speak English with a foreign accent?

Ruth. Well, I've only just noticed it. But I'm sure . . .

John. It's due to not opening their mouths properly.

Ruth. You won't face the facts, John, you . . .

Dr. Evans. Juveniles are very imitative. They are copying each other, obviously. It's a phase. Don't

5

worry. I haven't had a sixteen-year-old in my surgery for months. They seem a healthy lot.

Ruth. Oh, they're healthy. Lily's been in better health since her eyes went narrow, I'll say that, and since she started talking broken. But *I* haven't felt so well. I . . .

Dr. Evans. They speak Welsh?

John. Yes, they can speak Welsh.

Ruth. They learnt at school. This isn't Welsh that they speak, it's broken English.

Simon. My girl, Freda, has caught the habit. That, and her slit eyes, and her talk about the mountain when she comes home from work, it's driving us . . .

Ruth. Yes, they all go on about the mountain range. They've got to prepare for trouble, and all that. When you say, what trouble? — they don't answer.

Dr. Evans. What trouble?

Simon. How do we know what trouble? There's plenty trouble going on in this town, Doctor, if you'd only see it.

Dr. Evans. I see a good deal of what goes on here. I see all the children in the place sooner or later. My daughter sees them when she's home from school.

Ruth. How old is your Connie?

Dr. Evans. Close on sixteen.

Ruth. You'll see a change in her when she comes home for the holidays. . . .

Dr. Evans. Oh, I wouldn't predict . . .

Ruth. Their minds are funny, let's face it. They don't go near the dance-hall. I was never out of it, at their age.

Richard. They do their jobs all right, don't they? Mark Farmer is a good woodworker, but you'll never get the craftsmanship that we used to have when you only had your bit of timber and your lathe and your knife. Now I was talking to young Mark the other day, and slit eyes or not, he knows a good bit of work. I brought him inside this very room and I showed him this bowl of mine that the Eisteddfod rejected, and he said, 'Well,' he said . . .

Simon. It's not their jobs I'm worrying about. It's what they do with their spare time. What are they doing all Friday evenings up on the mountain and all Sunday afternoons? Freda's got a beautiful record player I gave her. Does she play it? No, she doesn't play it. She's up the bloody mountain with Lily David and all.

Ruth. My Lily isn't the same as she used to be. Once I said, 'Now, Lily, you don't want to go up the mountain with those others this week, you'll get yourself a bad name, give it a miss for once. Why don't you bring your friends home to tea?' I said. 'Up in the mountain, hail, rain or fine.' So she sat indoors all Sunday afternoon, believe me, and looked up at the mountains through the window, and then she looked at me with those narrow eyes. In the end I said, 'Go on, get up the bloody mountain then.' It gets me down. If it was a matter of sex you would know where you were. But I don't believe she's got any sex in her, the little cat.

John. That's a fact, right enough. They all give that impression. Don't upset yourself, Ruth.

Simon. . . . and when you ask what's going on up there they say, 'Eet ees dan-ger', like a refugee from Europe talking.

(A car draws up outside)

That will be the Reverend Pugh.

(A knock at the door)

Richard. Hughie Pugh.

Simon. That's not helpful, if you please, Richard.

(The bell rings)

Richard. When they don't get an answer to the knock, they ring. Just wait awhile — he'll ring again. They never knock twice, but they always ring twice.

Ruth. Put away the empties — quick.

(Ring and knock)

Simon. Answer it, Richard. Don't bother to hide those bottles, Ruth. He likes a drink, does Pugh.

Richard. Good gracious, they rang and they knocked. *(Shouts.)* Turn the handle and come in.

Ruth. I know he drinks but the empties look bad.

(Ring)

John. I'll go.

(Opens door)

Well, it's you after all, Margiad.

Simon. We thought you were the minister.

Richard. We thought you were Hughie Pugh. Good evening.

Margiad. There's a choir practice. Mr. Pugh's coming as soon as it's over. You were missed at the practice, Simon. There's a tenor short tonight.

Simon. I've no music left in me. Open a bottle of mineral water for Margiad, John.

8

Margiad. He'll be here any minute.

Dr. Evans. Who? Hugh Pugh?

Richard. Did h-you spew on Hughie Pugh?

Margiad. (*Slowly.*) Whose pew — did — Hughie — Pugh — hew? Ha-ha. Hoo-hoo.

Simon. Margiad!

Margiad. The water goes to my head, the first sip.

John. Ah, the water's not what it was during the war. There was a kick in it. . . .

Margiad. My God, Ruth. I can see the empties from here behind the chest.

Ruth. Can you? I thought I'd put them out of sight.

(*Re-arranges bottles*)

Is that better?

John. Let be. The Minister drinks. He takes a drink. Plenty. Now, we aren't getting any further, and . . .

(*A car draws up. Knock. Ring. Knock*)

Richard. Knock. Ring. Knock.

John. That's Mr. Pugh. Open the door.

Ruth. (*Sings.*) Open the door, Richard.

Margiad. You've had a drop too much, Ruth.

Richard. (*Opening the door.*) Come in, Mr. Pugh. Nice night. We've been waiting for you, Mr. Pugh.

Pugh. Well, here we are!

Ruth. Come and sit down, Mr. Pugh.

Margiad. It's late for you to come visiting. . . .

John. Open a bottle of mineral water for Mr. Pugh, Richard. You take a drink, don't you, Mr. Pugh?

Pugh. Oh, of course, these days. Times have changed. One must be broad-minded. *Half* a glass. *Thank* you. Oh, good evening, Dr. Evans. I didn't see you when I came in.

Dr. Evans. I wasn't here. I was out at the lavatory. Mineral water goes for the bladder.

Pugh. Would you say it's bad for the bladder?

Dr. Evans. Well, intoxicating liquor taken in any quantity . . .

Pugh. Yes, well now, what conclusions have we arrived at?

John. None. Ddim penderfyniad o gwbl. You see I can speak Welsh, Mr. Pugh, although I came from Yorkshire originally. . . .

Pugh. There is a barrier. And we must attempt to cross that barrier.

John.	Barrier.
Ruth.	. . . yes, barrier. We must . . .
Richard.	What barrier?
Dr. Evans.	Definitely a barrier . . .

Pugh. We must attempt to cross the barrier that stands between ourselves and those young girls and boys of ours. I must say, for myself, the last time my son was home from school I didn't notice any peculiarity about the eyes.

Ruth. Has he turned sixteen yet?

Pugh. Yes. Only just.

Ruth. You'll see a difference in your Thomas next week when he comes home for the holidays.

Pugh. Oh, I wouldn't predict . . . We mustn't be pessimistic, you know. I have a proposal to make.

Margiad. What's that, Mr. Pugh?

Pugh. What times do they go up the mountains? What days?

Ruth. Sunday afternoons.

John. Friday evenings.

Ruth. Friday evenings are the dangerous time.

Margiad. Now, Ruth.

Ruth. You know it's the danger. The children are full of it. Listen!

(Song from the mountain)

Ruth. There's the children coming home from the mountain.

Pugh. Danger . . . it's only a song . . .

Ruth. There's danger in it . . .

John. Ruth, you are getting hysterical.

Dr. Evans. Have the young people spoken of danger?

Ruth. They don't speak. They look dangerous. With their hair all cut short . . .

Dr. Evans. That's the fashion, Ruth. It's only the fashion.

Richard. Pass your glass, Ruth. It will calm you down.

(Glass noises)

A little more, Mr. Pugh? John?

Dr. Evans. I daresay they have some sexual experiences. Let's not beat about the bush. . . .

Ruth. Sex? No, it's danger. I can see it on their faces.

Margiad. You shouldn't speak of these things, Ruth.

Dr. Evans. What is Mr. Pugh's suggestion? Let's have it.

Pugh. But the mountain range isn't dangerous, is it? Not for your children who have grown up here, surely?

Ruth. It's a mysterious sort of danger.

John. Stop it, Ruth. Richard, put those bottles away. She's had too much.

Pugh. The age of sixteen is a strange sort of age. Sixteen — one-six. Six and one make seven. Seven is a mystical number.

Dr. Evans. Let's stick to facts. What is your suggestion, Mr. Pugh?

Pugh. I shall myself follow them up to the mountain range on Friday night and see what they are doing and saying. I shall not go in the capacity of spy, but shall attempt to have a chat with them, to cross the barrier.

Ruth. Oh no, you can't do that. . . . We've thought of that ourselves. We can't question them. It's dangerous.

Simon. God, yes, it's dangerous.

John. It doesn't do to probe too far, Mr. Pugh.

Margiad. It's dangerous, Mr. Pugh. Tell him, Dr. Evans, not to go.

Dr. Evans. I don't see why he shouldn't attempt to get on to terms. . . . I must say it's remarkable that you can't communicate with your own sons and daughters.

Margiad. } No, can't you see the danger?
Ruth. } . . . It's dangerous, Mr. Pugh. . . . Listen!

(*Fragment of song*)

John. Mr. Pugh, I think you'd better leave well alone.

Simon. Yes, give it a miss.

Dr. Evans. This is ridiculous. Here's Pugh in his good pastoral office, going to see what he can do to settle this misunderstanding. . . .

Margiad. There isn't any misunderstanding because there isn't any ground of understanding.

Ruth. There's only the facts.

John. Facts. Slit eyes.

Simon. Foreign speech. Facts.

Richard. Well, speaking as a bachelor craftsman, I'd say the facts are such that Hughie Pugh, as minister of this parish, might do well to look into things.

Margiad. It's nothing to do with you, Richard, you're only a bachelor. On paper, that's to say . . .

Ruth. Yes, he's only a bachelor. Never done a day's work in his . . .

Pugh. I didn't like the way you addressed me, Richard, just now.

Richard. Hughie Pugh?

Pugh. Mr. Pugh to you.

Richard. Long live Wales! I hope you don't get into a stew.

Ruth. Listen!

(*Song from the mountain*)

2. THE MOUNTAIN SIDE

(*Song becoming loud and merging with footsteps climbing the mountain*)

Mark. Halt!

(*Rustles paper*)

Lily David.

Lily. Here.

Mark. Freda Rhys.

Freda. Here.

Mark. Jones.

Jones. Here.

Mark. Lily, bring the torch closer a bit — yes. (*Reads.*) Thomas Pugh (*pronounces it 'Pug'*).

Thomas. Pugh.

Mark. Thomas *Pugh*. Age, please?

Thomas. Sixteen last week.

Mark. Place of residence?

Thomas. The Valley.

Mark. Occupation of parent or guardian?

Thomas. My father's the parson down there. (*Laughs slightly.*)

Mark. (*Laughs.*) But why did you not report last week?

Thomas. I've been away at a school. (*Laughs.*) Now I'm home for the holidays.

(*Others laugh*)

Mark. Yes, it's a great fantasy. But it's getting serious. Who's that girl there? I haven't seen her here before.

Connie. Connie Evans.

Mark. Connie Evans.

(*Rustles paper*)

Shine the torch, Lily. Yes, I see. Age, please.

Connie. Sixteen years and five weeks.

Mark. Why haven't you reported before?

Connie. I've been away at school. My sister keeps a school across the river.

Mark. Mad?

Connie. Well, childish.

Mark. Occupation of parent or guardian?

Connie. My father's the doctor in the Valley. (*Laughs.*) Dr. Evans.

Mark. Mad?

Connie. Oh, yes — childish.

Mark. My name's Mark Farmer. My uncle's John Farmer — he's the Town Surveyor.

(*All laugh*)

Have you met Jones? Son of Richard Jones, the bachelor craftsman.

Connie. Yes; hallo, Jones.

Thomas. Hallo, Jones.

Jones. Glad you've come. We've been waiting for you.

Mark. Jones does all the negotiating.

Jones. We'll be wanting a fire. Collect some wood. Then on to the caves.

(*Footsteps on the mountain. Then entering the caves. Sound of running water*)

Thomas. I remember these caves. Isn't that a mineral spring? I could do with a drink.

Freda. Oh, no. . . .

Jones. Don't drink.

Connie. Oh, can't we have a drink? I'm thirsty.

Jones. You mustn't drink from the mineral spring. It makes madness.

Freda. Who's got the twigs? We'll light the fire. (*Sings.*) . . . Since she went to the Danger Zone. . . .

(*Hums rest of tune interrupted by Jones*)

Jones. Sit round. Freda — there. Lily — there. Mark, over here. Thomas, next to me. Connie, next to him. Now the first question tonight is what's to be done about those people down in the Valley.

Mark. They've got to be humoured, of course, for the time being.

Freda. It can't go on much longer. The situation's becoming impossible.

Lily. Connie, you understand that they think they are living in Wales.

Jones. That's to say, out of the Danger Zone.

Connie. Safely in Wales. But I always knew . . . and when I came home from school I was sure . . .

Thomas. (*Laughs.*) Safely in Wales. Do you know, my father thinks he can do something about us.

Lily. (*Mimicking.*) There's hallucination.

Connie. *There's* hallucination.

Thomas. I heard him saying, 'I daresay they are up to some adolescent sexual practices.'

Jones. That's all they can think about — sex.

Mark. It keeps them occupied.

Freda. How long for? That's the question.

Jones. It depends how long we can hold back the Danger. Of course, the Danger's bound to come, but we need time to pave the way.

Freda. Yes, it is just a question of time.

Thomas. I'm awfully thirsty.

Jones. You'll have to be thirsty. You can't drink this stuff.

Connie. *I'm* thirsty.

Jones. Everyone's thirsty their first time in the Danger Zone.

Freda. Yes, Jones is right — honestly. You won't notice it after a bit. It's only your first time up that you feel like this — isn't it, Lily?

Lily. Here, suck a mint. Don't touch that mineral water.

Thomas. What does the Danger look like?

Jones. There's nothing much to look at. He looks like us. He wears his hair long.

Mark. (*Half-laughs.*) Then he can't look like us.

Jones. Hair longer than ordinary isn't so different from hair shorter than ordinary, somehow.

Freda. } Yes, that's true. . . .
Lily. } . . . yes, I see what you mean.

Mark. A touch of austerity.

Jones. Yes, that must be it.

Freda. Are we very austere, Jones?

Jones. Yes.

Lily. ⎱ How young is the Danger-Boy?
Freda. ⎰ ... how old is ...

Jones. He might be seventeen, eighteen.

Thomas. What are his clothes like?

Jones. He wears ...

Mark. He wears a shirt and blue jeans in the summer — isn't that right, Jones? And in the winter he wears corduroys and a grey duffle. Jones tried to get a grey duffle last winter but he could only get a brown one. Didn't you say he has a tartan shirt, Jones?

Jones. I think so.

Connie. I'm fond of tartan, you know, I ...

Lily. ⎱ Yes, it brightens up the passing scene.
Freda. ⎰ I like a nice *red* tartan, not one of the ...

Jones. He's thin. He's very thin.

(Silence)

Mark. Yes.

Lily. Yes, well, that's understandable.

Connie. Is he thinner than us?

Jones. Yes. But we'll be thinner than we are, it's inevitable. You realise that, don't you, Connie? ... Thomas?

Mark. You don't get fat on poverty.

Thomas. What about the rest of them, over the mountain?

Jones. I haven't seen the others, Thomas.

Mark. We'll see them in time.

Lily. Jones — you're very gloomy tonight. Where's your guitar?

Jones. (*Plucks guitar as he speaks.*) We can't keep up the parley forever. Sooner or later they'll come, and that's all right — but what if they come too soon? What will the people in the valley do?

Mark. Give them lots to drink, I expect.

Jones. The Danger mustn't drink. You know, they could simply walk over the mountains and . . .

Mark. They'll march over the mountains and descend . . .

Jones. They'll *walk* over the mountains and down to the Valley. Why should they march? All they need to do is pick their way over the rocks — it's easy.

Freda. What will my mother and father do? Simon Rhys, tenor in the choir. Margiad Rhys, houseproud, and what a saver!

Lily. I often wonder if my mother will marry again. It's going to be terrible for them all when they realise they aren't living quite in Wales.

Connie. Do you know, I always had the feeling that it wasn't quite the Wales we thought it was.

Thomas. So did I. My father says the landscape reminds him of Central Europe. The mountain border country, you know. He used to do a lot of climbing.

Mark. It's a big responsibility. They've got to be enlightened sooner or later.

Jones. (*Stops playing.*) Have you got the sacks?

Freda. Oh, is it time already?

Jones. Yes. Bring the sacks. Put out the fire, Mark.

Thomas. What are the sacks for?

Jones. We fill them with roots. Those people need roots on the other side of the mountain. It's one of the conditions of the parley. It's all too rocky over on their side and they can't get the root vegetables. They've a hard time of it.

Freda. Poor things.

Jones. They've got very little to feed their goats on.

Lily. I don't wonder they want to come over to us.

Jones. Have you got the spades and trowels?

(*Picking up spades and trowels*)

Thomas. Where do we dig?

Jones. Further up the mountain, along the ridge where the soil's good. The forestry commission has planted it out, there are plenty of good roots up there. Let's go.

(*Sings.*) . . . Gone to skin and bone
         . . . Since — she — went . . .

(*Plodding up the mountain*)

Thomas. There are sheep up on the ridge, aren't there?

Jones. Yes, they're fast asleep.

Thomas. What about the old shepherd man?

Jones. Old Ham? — He's always asleep in his hut. He never hears us.

Freda. Except on Sunday afternoons. Then he just looks at us.

Connie. Do you dig for roots on Sunday afternoons?

Mark. No, only on Friday nights. On . . .

Lily. On Sundays we just come up here for the climb.

Thomas.⎫
Connie.⎬ What for?

Jones. Exercise. We don't always come up the mountain for a set purpose, you know. We've got to have some recreation. Friday nights, a set purpose. Sundays, a walk in the rain or whatever it is.

(*Sound of running water*)

Thomas. Where's that water? I hear water.

Jones. This is the source of the mineral spring, just here. Don't drink it — don't you know it sends you mad? Do you want to become like the generation down in the Valley? Mad with their hallucinations? Feeling safe in the Danger Zone they don't believe in?

Thomas. I only wanted a drink.

Connie. Me too.

Freda. Jones, could we stop a minute?

Jones. Yes, what for?

Freda. There's something we ought to get settled.

Mark. Halt.

Freda. Jones, it's just the question of the peace offering.

Jones. What peace offering?

Freda. When you go over the top to parley with the Danger tonight.

Jones. I'm going to take some roots. They want roots in the Danger Zone. Let's get on with it, and dig up the . . .

Connie. Oh, *let's* get on with it. I'm frightened. We're so near the top, and all this moonlight . . .

21

Thomas. What's that on the ridge — in that field? It's a camp! They've come!

Jones. Come back, Thomas. It's only the sheep sleeping in the field.

Freda. What about the peace offering? What about it, Jones?

Jones. Well, what about it?

Freda. Take a flask of mineral water as an offering. Take it, Jones.

Jones. No, the Danger mustn't drink. That's all decided and settled. If I'm going to parley with the Danger-Boy I'm going to do it clean.

Lily. Well, Jones, it seems fair enough, as Freda says. You stick a bottle of mineral water in among the roots at the bottom of the sack, and if they drink it, fair enough. If they don't, we're no worse off, are we? It's . . .

Freda. Let them go off their heads, then they'll stop worrying us. What are we going to do about the generation down there in the Valley if the Danger Zone marches in?

Jones. They won't march, they'll walk.

Thomas. I should have thought that any way of withholding the enemy was a fair one.

Jones. You should have thought . . . Those people are not the enemy, they are the Danger. If the Danger drinks the stuff we'll be thoroughly isolated. Just a handful of us in a world of derangement.

Lily. Sometimes I'd rather . . .

Freda. Sometimes I think I'd like to have a delusion just by way of a break.

Jones. I can't offer that poison to the Danger-Boy. It's against the Geneva Convention, is that understood?

Mark. Yes, I think it's understood. It would be a pity to change the character of the Danger. We wouldn't have anyone to parley with. Let's go and dig those roots up.

Freda. He might not parley much longer. How do we know what his next demands are going to be?

Jones. We shall know tonight. He said he'd have a new demand.

Mark. I thought he wouldn't be content with roots for long.

Jones. On we go. Over there, Lily, start digging there. Connie, here's a patch where we started last week, it'll be easier for you. . . .

3. THE MOUNTAIN TOP

Jones. (*Climbing and humming snatch of tune. Puts down sacks.*) There you are, Danger-Boy.

Danger-Boy. Hallo, Jones. Nice night. Big moon.

Jones. I've brought the roots.

Danger-Boy. Any parsnips?

Jones. No. Do you want parsnips particularly?

Danger-Boy. We could do with some parsnips.

Jones. Cigarette?

Danger-Boy. Thanks. I could do with a cigarette.

Jones. You can keep the packet.

Danger-Boy. Thanks. Sit down. Did you bring the liquor?

Jones. No, sorry. I can't get hold of the liquor. The stream has dried up.

Danger-Boy. Every time I come up here to the crest I hear running water.

Jones. That's not the mineral stream, it's the sheep-pond lapping in the wind.

Danger-Boy. We had rain yesterday.

Jones. We didn't.

Danger-Boy. Didn't you? Don't you ever have rain?

Jones. Sometimes.

Danger-Boy. And then the mineral spring isn't dry any more?

Jones. No.

Danger-Boy. But you never bring me any mineral water.

Jones. No, it's polluted. We never touch the stuff ourselves.

Danger-Boy. Look, Jones, I just want a drop for myself. It isn't for general distribution.

Jones. Look, Danger-Boy, let's keep this conversation on a business footing.

Danger-Boy. All right. We're coming soon, you know. We'll walk down the mountain side and . . .

Jones. We need time, Danger-Boy. We've got to prepare the Valley population for people like you. They have a bad enough time trying to understand people like us.

Danger-Boy. They would get used to it.

Jones. You couldn't breathe at that level. It's bad enough for us — for Lily and Mark and Freda and

Thomas Pugh and Connie Evans. But when we get more established . . .

Danger-Boy. Who are Thomas and Connie?

Jones. They are new. Just turned sixteen. They've been away at school and have just come home.

Danger-Boy. Are they feeling the strain?

Jones. Well, imagine for yourself . . .

Danger-Boy. Yes, I know. We don't have that difficulty on our side. No drunken elders with hallucinations. But then we haven't got good soil, Jones.

Jones. I know.

Danger-Boy. My crowd's anxious to be on the move. The soil's too rocky. We're as bored as hell. We can't survive like this. . . .

Jones. Do you know what would happen if you all walked down the mountain tomorrow and along the streets of the town?

Danger-Boy. What?

Jones. Mr. Simon Rhys would dial 999.

Danger-Boy. Oh.

Jones. Mr. Simon Rhys's house would be the first one you would pass. He used to be a miner but he got his face blown up in an accident, and he got compensation and had his face patched up. Now he breeds greyhounds. He's doing well. He's had the telephone installed.

Danger-Boy. Really?

Jones. Mrs. Ruth David has got a washing machine.

Danger-Boy. No!

c   25

Jones. Yes. Margiad Rhys has got an iron that moves over the ironing board by itself.

Danger-Boy. Really?

Jones. John Farmer has got a Ford Zephyr.

Danger-Boy. Really?

Jones. Dr. Evans has got a Jaguar.

Danger-Boy. Really? Hasn't anyone got a Maserati down there?

Jones. No, they haven't got a Maserati. The Rev. Pugh has got a Renault and a motor mower.

Danger-Boy. Really?

Jones. They've all got television except my father, who's a bachelor, and rather old-fashioned.

Danger-Boy. Ah.

Jones. Can you spare a cigarette out of that packet I gave you? — Mr. Simon Rhys has got round blue eyes.

Danger-Boy. Really? In spite of the mining accident?

Jones. Yes. Do you know how he talks? You'd laugh. (*Mimic.*) Ower chidr-en are grow-ing dot-ty.

Danger-Boy. Is he mad?

Jones. Yes, they are all mad.

(*Pause*)

Danger-Boy. Nice evening. Sit down.

Jones. Yes, I think I will. Thanks.

Danger-Boy. We want a hostage.

Jones. What?

Danger-Boy. We want you to give us a hostage.

Jones. Why?

26

Danger-Boy. Oh, just in case you were thinking of fooling around with us in any way.

Jones. I was afraid of this.

Danger-Boy. Yes, it's a protection against 999.

Jones. Which one of us?

Danger-Boy. One of the mad ones with the round eyes.

Jones. Now look here. We've been brought up to feel guilty about our parents. They taught us guilt as a safeguard for themselves. We can't let them down now. We'd feel more guilty than ever. You can't have one of them.

Danger-Boy. We'd give him good treatment, Jones.

Jones. But you're dangerous.

Danger-Boy. Yes, well, there are worse things than being dangerous, from what I know of the safe people.

Jones. You'll have to accept one of us. You can't have the older generation. Take me. Take Mark. Take Freda.

Danger-Boy. Who is it you are trying to protect from us? Are you trying to protect yourselves?

Jones. No, we don't mind you particularly. It makes no difference if you live this side of the mountain or that side. It's just . . .

Danger-Boy. The older generation with the round eyes.

Jones. Yes. They drink this mineral water, and they . . .

Danger-Boy. Then we'll have one of the round-eyed ones. My boys are getting impatient. Next Friday, I suggest.

Jones. I'll have to talk this over with my friends. I can't promise — it's unlikely.

Danger-Boy. It's urgent, Jones. Talk it over, and say it's urgent. Listen, Jones, a personal matter — it might help us to smooth things out — the mineral water. If you brought . . .

Jones. No, it's poison. You can't have it. It's against the Geneva . . .

Danger-Boy. Only for myself. A taste . . .

Jones. Sorry, it can't be done. The stuff's dangerous. We've got enough sufferers around us already.

Danger-Boy. Dangerous. . . .

Jones. Yes, well, I mean dangerous to you and me. People like us.

Danger-Boy. Oh well, next Friday then. . . .

Jones. Next Friday.

Danger-Boy. And don't forget to bring the parsnips.

4. THE VALLEY

(*Bottle noises in Richard's parlour*)

Richard. Have a drop more, Ruth.

Ruth. Thanks, dear, thanks. Oh, it's nice, Richard.

Richard. You and me will get talked about if the company doesn't arrive soon. It isn't often I'm alone with a fine-looking widow in my house.

Ruth. Here's to your health, Richard, and you just keep your remarks to yourself.

Richard. And my thoughts to myself as well.

Ruth. I'm a lonely woman, Richard, and there's my girl Lily gone strange like the others.

Richard. Speaking as a bachelor craftsman, it would seem to me that this is a phase that they are going through, no more.

Ruth. You can't change the shape of their eyes. And the sound of their foreign tongues. I wonder what Mr. Pugh found out when he followed them up last Friday? If indeed he went.

Richard. Yes, he's a good old Peeping Tom is Hughie Pugh. I'd like to give him something to peep on if he was peeping through that keyhole at this moment.

Ruth. You keep your mouth clean. . . .

Richard. Now, Ruth . . .

Ruth. And your hands to yourself. Don't you realise there's a danger we've come to discuss?

Richard. I was always a dangerous fellow myself, Ruth. There's my boy Jones without a mother to his name, remember. Now you and me have got a mutual interest in these young people and we might very well go up the mountain ourselves to satisfy our minds. How about that, Ruth? You're a fine-built widow for a walk with. We could get to the top of that mountain on a Sunday afternoon and see right over to Glamorgan-shire. What about it, Ruth? Have a drink, Ruth.

(*Sound of glasses*)

Ruth. I've no sport left in me, Richard. And there's nothing to discover about their Sunday afternoons. It's their Friday nights I'm afraid of.

Richard. Do they get back late on Fridays?

Ruth. No, my Lily returns at nine o'clock, but she looks as if, somehow, the time that's passed up there is longer than the time that's passed at home.

Richard. Oh, they've been having their fun and games on a Friday night. And what's wrong with a bit of sex, Ruth? It's nature. Speaking as a bachelor craftsman, you put thoughts into my head yourself.

Ruth. Go on with you, Richard.

Pugh. (*Approaching with Dr. Evans.*) I could hardly believe my eyes and ears when that boy . . .

Richard. Come in, come in. You didn't knock, ring, knock.

Pugh. I beg your pardon. The door was open. You see, we're all a little put out, a little . . .

Dr. Evans. Ruth, have you seen my girl since she came home from school? Have you just had a look at her?

Ruth. No, I haven't seen Connie.

Pugh. Have you seen my son? May the good Lord preserve . . .

Richard. Have your kids gone funny like the rest?

Pugh. Funny . . .!

Dr. Evans. I'm glad her mother isn't alive to see it. Narrow eyes. Broken English . . .

Ruth. How did you find things up on the mountain last night, Mr. Pugh?

Pugh. I didn't go.

(*Sound of glasses*)

Richard. Mineral water — excuse me, Ruth, there's the opener just behind you. . . . Ta. So you didn't go, Mr. Pugh?

Pugh. No, I didn't go. I was too put out by seeing Thomas.

Richard. You funked it, Hughie Pugh.

Ruth. Oh, the danger, the danger!

        (*Ring. Knock. Ring*)

Richard. You got cold feet, Hughie . . .?

Pugh. No, it was just that I was a bit upset last night. I . . .

Dr. Evans. Let sleeping dogs lie, that's what I say. There's some psychological cause behind all this. Doesn't bear looking into.

        (*Knock. Ring. Knock*)

Richard. Knock, ring, knock.

Ruth. Let them in.

Richard. (*At the door.*) Good evening, Margiad Rhys, Simon, good evening. John Farmer, come in. . . .

        (*Fade briefly as for the same evening*)

Richard. One for the road, then, John.

John. Thanks.

Richard. Mr. Pugh, one for the road.

Pugh. Thanks.

John. I don't see that it matters, Mr. Pugh.

Dr. Evans. Let sleeping dogs lie, that's what I . . .

Simon. Somebody's got to bridge that gap.

Pugh. Next Friday night, for certain, I'm going.

Margiad. Why don't all you men go and face it?

Pugh. Face what?

Ruth. The danger . . .

Pugh. There's no danger. Keep calm, please. Our youth are hardly likely to open their hearts to a whole deputation. One must go. It's only a matter of finding out what these young people are up to, and talking to them . . .

Dr. Evans. Reasonably. . . .

Margiad. Nice and soft. . . .

Richard. Not in haste or in anger. . . .

Ruth. Perfectly calm. . . .

John. Approaching as it were on tiptoe. . . .

(*Fade*)

5. THE MOUNTAIN SIDE

(*Friday: in the caves*)

Jones. Just a minute. I thought I heard a noise. . . .

(*Silence*)

A rustle. Lily, shine the torch. Just outside the cave.

Lily. There's nothing.

Jones. It's a war of nerves, all right.

Freda. Oh, Jones, your nerves are not giving way, are they?

Jones. No.

Mark. Well, carry on, Jones.

Jones. They want parsnips.

Connie. As well as a hostage?

Jones. I heard a definite rustle. Behind that rock, there. . . .

Lily. Where?

Connie. Listen!

(*Drinking sound*)

Oh, could it be the Danger? Could he come down here to the caves all on his own. Could he? I . . .

Mark. ⎱ Quiet, Connie.
Jones. ⎰ Quiet, Connie. We haven't *time* for panic. Shine the torch, Lily.

Lily. I don't see anyone.

Jones. Sit down. All sit in your places. Now what's to be done?

Connie. Won't they take one of us? I'll go for a hostage, honestly. . . .

Thomas. Well, I suppose it should be me, as the youngest man. . . .

Jones. Danger-Boy wants an older man. With round eyes.

Mark. That's going to be difficult.

Jones. I know it's going to be difficult.

Freda. We can't very well kidnap our own fathers.

Connie. (*Giggles.*) Imagine it.

Jones. There's a man at the mouth of the cave lying on the ground.

Mark. Where?

Jones. Over there, lying flat on his face.

Mark. It's only a shadow of the rock in the moon-light.

(*Sound of drinking*)

Jones. He's drinking from the brook.

Freda. Goodness, it's . . .

Thomas. Father!

33

Pugh. (*Approaching.*) Good evening, boys and girls. I was just refreshing myself at the life-giving stream. Well, now, how are we? I thought we might have a chat . . .

Thomas. Father, go home.

Pugh. I come in peace, my children. What a jolly camp fire! Well, I thought we might have a chat. May I join you?

(*Silence*)

Thanks. I'll just — I think — sit here — beside you, Jones. Just think of me as one of yourselves, won't you?

(*Silence*)

Very gay. Well, how are things?

(*Silence*)

I'm so glad. Well, that's splendid. When I was a lad very often things between the younger generation and the older reached a point of, well, strain. A chat with someone older and wiser can often ease the tension. I feel — don't you? — there's a gap to be bridged. I must say, it's very heartening to see you young folks seated round a camp fire up here in the caves, and I've no doubt you've been singing as I and my companions used to do as lads. You've been singing together round the fire, haven't you? I see you've got your guitar there, Jones.

(*Silence*)

Very gay. And you've been telling camp-fire tales, I'll be bound. Building up the adventures of the mind. And why not? How I wish I were young again! Excitement, adventure, danger. . . . Do you know,

34

Jones, as I came up the mountain tonight, as I approached your splendid hide-out, I overheard you telling your story, I heard the words 'danger', 'hostage' — magic words! How my imagination and memory were fired! Do carry on, Jones, with your story. I haven't come to disrupt your Friday rituals, you know.

Jones. It's time for me to be off. I've got an appointment. You'd better go back, Mr. Pugh.

Thomas. Go home, Father.

Freda. There's danger here, Mr. Pugh.

Pugh. Danger? Well, I think, my dear, I can face any dangers as might lurk amongst these familiar mountain reaches. . . .

Jones. I'll see you later.

Mark. What are you going to say to him, Jones?

Jones. I'll tell him it can't be done.

Pugh. Where are you off to, Jones?

Jones. Up to the crest of the mountain to meet the Danger-Boy.

Pugh. Dear me, how exciting! I'll come with you, if I may. First I must have a little drink. This water so near the source is absolutely intoxicating. Wait for me, Jones. I shan't be a jiffy.

(*Drinks as Jones departs*)

That's better. Now where has Jones gone? Which way?

Mark. Hold him.

Pugh. Look here, now look here, I can't have violence. This is the very thing that gets you young folk a bad

35

name. Release me immediately. Violence is the one thing I won't . . . Let me go! I'm surprised at *you*, Thomas. Release my arms. . . .

Mark. You can't go with Jones, Mr. Pugh. It's dangerous.

Pugh. Very well, I shan't go with Jones. Let go of my arms. Let me out of this cave, all of you.

Mark. Don't release him till Jones is out of sight. The moon's strong.

Connie. Jones has gone now, Mark.

Freda. Yes, he's out of sight.

Mark. Let him go. Now, Mr. Pugh, you . . .

Pugh. That was going too far, you know. I have had no intention of prying into your private affairs; it was a simple act of friendship my coming here to hold out a helping hand.

Mark. You'd better go down the mountain now, Mr. Pugh. We'd rather you did.

Thomas. It's for your own good . . .

Freda. I don't see why we shouldn't let him go to the place where Jones has gone. Let him be the hostage.

Pugh. My dears, if you had told me this was a game I would have perfectly understood. Of course I will play the hostage. Why don't you trust me?

Freda. Do you want to know all about the game, Mr. Pugh?

Mark. Freda!

Freda. (*With forced naïvety.*) Well, there's a race of people living on the other side of the mountain, Mr. Pugh, and if we don't provide a hostage they're going

36

sheep touched by the moon, and old Ham's hut in the circle of trees. And over there, on the other side of the mountain, a wooded path. The tears, Jones, at the heart of things. . . . Is someone climbing up the path? That will be your friend. I didn't realise you had a *real* assignment. . . .

Jones. Go back at once, Mr. Pugh.

Pugh. A nice tall lad. Coming to his rendezvous. And I'm to be the hostage.

Jones. What are you saying?

Pugh. Your games . . . your dream world . . . how my youth comes back to me! Do you read Byron, Jones?

Jones. I haven't much spare time. Look, Mr. Pugh, this is dangerous.

(*Footsteps approach up the mountain*)

Pugh. (*Recites.*)
> Our life is two-fold; Sleep hath its own world,
> A boundary between the things misnamed
> Death and existence: Sleep hath its own world,
> And a wide realm of wild reality.
> And dreams in their development have breath,
> And tears, and tortures, and the touch of joy;
> They leave a weight upon our waking thoughts,
> They take a weight from off our waking toils,
> They do divide our being; they become
> A portion of ourselves as of our time,
> And look like heralds of eternity.

Danger-Boy. (*Approaching.*) Hallo, Jones. Have you brought the parsnips?

Pugh. (*Laughs.*) No, he's brought the parson. (*Laughs.*)

Danger-Boy. Oh! . . . Is this the hostage, Jones?

Jones.⎫ No.
Pugh. ⎭ Yes.

Danger-Boy. Oh, what round eyes you've got!

Pugh. What *is* the game? I really do want to enter into the spirit of the thing. Why do you want a hostage? Put me in the picture and I'm ready to fall in. Pugh's my name. I have a son your age.

Danger-Boy. You'll be all right with us, Mr. Pugh. My boys want a hostage in order to hasten the parley between Jones and me. We want to come down and occupy your Valley. Jones's gang want to delay us. That's the position so far.

Pugh. Most exciting. I hope it won't come to a brawl.

Danger-Boy. Oh, it won't come to a brawl. It's a walk-over for us.

Jones. Look, Danger-Boy, Mr. Pugh here doesn't realise the seriousness . . .

Pugh. Nonsense, Jones. I'm in dead earnest. I've been young once myself, you know. I . . .

Danger-Boy. Jones — Jones. Did you bring me any of the stuff?

Jones. No.

Danger-Boy. It's only a personal favour I'm asking, Jones. I'm quite strong-minded enough to withstand any harmful effect of your mineral water. I'm sure it's grossly exaggerated. . . .

Pugh. Mineral water? Haven't you tasted our marvellous water? My dear boy, it's the finest spring in Wales, nay, Europe. I strongly recommend it for its revitalising qualities. My veins are brimming with it. Never a day

40

passes but I drink several glasses of this beautiful natural water of ours from the richest mineral spring in Europe. It courses through the blood, my boy. You austere young people don't know what you're missing.

Danger-Boy. Have you got any on you?

Pugh. No, alas, I haven't. (*Laughs.*) But I've got plenty inside me, oh, yes. Jones, why don't you fetch some mineral water for your friend. . . .

Jones. It's poison. I've told you, Danger-Boy. It's against the rules.

Pugh. Oh well, I suppose one must abide by the rules of the game. What are your rules, by the way?

Jones. Poverty. Chastity. Obedience. And no taking of mineral water or inciting others to take it.

Pugh. Good gracious me!

Danger-Boy. We must be getting along, then, Mr. Pugh. I'll make him comfortable, Jones. See you on Friday next.

Pugh. Oh, I . . . do you want me to come with you now? It's rather late. Can't we continue this tomorrow afternoon? I have some correspondence to attend to, and . . .

Jones. He doesn't want to be a hostage, Danger-Boy. And we don't see our way to letting you have a hostage from amongst his generation. Very sorry, but . . .

Pugh. Not at all, not at all. If you really intend to proceed with your . . . *mythos* — I have served in the war, you know, and I've taken part in manœuvres, it's the same thing — of course we must carry them through. All night, if necessary. What a lark!

Jones. Mr. Pugh, you would be away a long time. Weeks, perhaps.

Danger-Boy. Perhaps not so long as that, Jones.

Pugh. Boys, I perfectly understand the convention. Weeks, months, years, call them what you will. I insist on accompanying Dangerfield here. I would like to meet his gang very much this evening.

Jones. His name's Danger-Boy.

Pugh. Danger-Boy. (*Fading out.*) And on our way, Dangerside and I will have a good talk. . . .

7. THE VALLEY

(*Richard's cottage*)

Evans. And when did you last see your father?

Thomas. Last Friday night.

Ruth. Something's happened to him, I feel sure. I knew there was danger. . . .

Thomas. He left us about eight o'clock.

Margiad. But what were you doing up there in the cave?

Thomas. Discussing things.

Ruth. ⎫ Discussing things!
Dr. Evans. ⎭ Which way did he go?

Thomas. He started to climb down the mountain. But Freda Rhys says he changed his mind and climbed up to the top.

Simon. Why should he climb to the top at that time of night?

Thomas. Jones had gone up there.

Ruth. ⎫
Margiad. ⎭ What for?

Thomas. To discuss things with a friend.

John. It's all damned mysterious. Let's fill your glass, Ruth. Margiad? Dr. Evans? Just a minute till I open a fresh . . .

Dr. Evans. Don't look so worried, my boy.

Thomas. Well, I'd like to know what's happened to my father.

Richard. Hugh Pugh's a good climber, isn't he? I imagine he's just gone on a tour of the mountain range. One ought to see a bit more of Wales this weather.

Ruth. He's come to grief! I knew there was danger . . .

Margiad. There's danger somewhere . . .

John. We must inform the police.

Dr. Evans. Organise a search.

Simon. Get cracking, then, man.

Richard. Don't do anything hasty, now. Those mountains are perfectly safe for a man like Hughie Pugh. The mountains are safe for anyone.

Margiad. Well, *you* ought to know, Richard.

Ruth. What the hell do you mean by that, Margiad?

Margiad. *You* ought to know, Ruth. You're up in the mountains often enough these fine afternoons, both of you.

Ruth. You're drawing conclusions, aren't you?

Richard. Ruth and I go up to exercise our limbs and to bottle some of the mineral spring from the source, and we have nothing to conceal.

Dr. Evans. Let us attend to the matter in hand. We shall inform the police.

John. Organise a search.

Ruth. Run to the police station.

Margiad. Ring 999.

Richard. Speaking as a bachelor craftsman, I would proceed with caution.

(*Fade*)

8. THE MOUNTAIN SIDE

(*Jones playing guitar*)

Freda. A nice way to spend a Sunday afternoon, I must say, sitting here in the cave watching the whole population combing the mountain side in search of Hughie Pugh. It's awful watching a lot of people looking for someone you know they won't find. I think it's what a murderer must feel when he's standing by watching the investigations.

Lily. I miss my walk. I like my walk on Sunday afternoon.

Connie. I'd like a nice game of . . .

Jones. Well, you can't have it.

Mark. What did the Danger-Boy say on Friday, Jones, about Hughie Pugh? Is he all right over there?

(*No answer. Jones stops playing*)

Jones. On Sunday afternoons we don't discuss politics, religion, mythology, psychology . . .

Mark. I know, Jones, but it's only Mr. Pugh — I . . .

Jones. Or sociology.

(*Starts playing*)

44

Mark. I know, Jones, but this is a bit of an emergency. The whole town's out looking for Pugh.

Jones. They won't find him.

Mark. I know, but . . .

Lily. He isn't in Wales. They are looking for him in Wales.

Mark. I know, Lily, but we ought to know what's happened to him, how he's living and all that. Didn't the Danger-Boy give you some idea, Jones?

Thomas. I think I'm entitled to some news of my father.

Jones. (*Stops playing.*) I met him as usual, same time, same place. . . .

9. THE MOUNTAIN TOP

Danger-Boy. Jones — is that you, Jones?

Jones. Yes. I've brought some carrots. What's the matter?

Danger-Boy. Nothing, Jones.

Jones. I thought you sounded nervous. How's the hostage?

Danger-Boy. He's fine, Jones. We all like Mr. Pugh, Jones. What eloquence and fire! It's amazing what that mineral water does to a man.

Jones. I'd like to get down to business tonight, Danger-Boy. You've got the hostage. We can start talking terms from where we left off. Now supposing we agree to a gradual infiltration from your side, starting off, let's say, with three or four men. But first of all . . .

45

Danger-Boy. Jones, did you bring any mineral water with you, Jones?

Jones. . . . but first of all we've got to define the frontier once and for all, otherwise there's going to be a muddle.

Danger-Boy. Our boys are going to do away with the frontier.

Jones. Yes, quite — in time. But before you can do away with it you've got to have a frontier. I've marked the map here — just move the torch — thanks — now look at this line. I think we're agreed up to this point here, where the pine forest . . .

Danger-Boy. Jones, we want mineral water. Mr. Pugh has been telling us so much . . .

Jones. You can't have it. It's polluted. It sends people off their heads.

Danger-Boy. The water contains the richest deposits in the world, Mr. Pugh says, Jones.

Jones. Mr. Pugh says . . .! Mr. Pugh is mad with the stuff.

Danger-Boy. It fills his veins.

Jones. It circulates through his system. . . .

Danger-Boy. His blood is loaded with the substance. . . .

Jones. His stomach is lined with it. . . .

Danger-Boy. It surges through his brain. . . .

Jones. His very spittle is laced with it. . . .

Danger-Boy. I know. That's what Mr. Pugh said. Mineral water . . .

Jones. But he's drunk with it. He suffers from delusions, Danger-Boy.

46

Danger-Boy. Jones, we don't think so, Jones.

Jones. What do you mean?

Danger-Boy. We want to come down to your Valley, Jones.

Jones. Exactly. Well, first we've got to make an agreement, and do the thing gradually, so that the older generation . . .

Danger-Boy. We want mineral water, Jones. We are craving . . .

Jones. You can't have it, Danger-Boy. That's completely out. Do you want to become like the people of the old world — money, comfort, success, lust, self-indulgence . . .?

Danger-Boy. Mr. Pugh has a different story, Jones.

Jones. I'm afraid we've reached a deadlock, then, for tonight.

Danger-Boy. No.

Jones. But obviously . . .

Danger-Boy. We have an ultimatum. Either you bring us a supply of mineral water by Sunday morning or else. A good supply.

Jones. You mean that you are prepared to invade the Valley on Sunday morning?

Danger-Boy. No, quite honestly, we are not prepared. The truth is, Jones, a lot of us are too full of boredom to move. The soil has been difficult to work. Conditions like ours obstruct the will. What we want is mineral water. Then we'll come!

Jones. Are you proposing to send Mr. Pugh over the mountain to fetch it?

Danger-Boy. No, Jones, not our hostage. He would just walk off to his house in Wales if we let him over the mountain. We still have our wits about us, Jones.

Jones. Then I don't see that there's any ultimatum. It's . . .

Danger-Boy. We've decided. If we can't get the water to drink by Sunday at noon, we'll drink Mr. Pugh.

Jones. What's that you're saying?

Danger-Boy. His blood is full. His veins are flowing. The deposits are rich. It circulates his system. Jones, listen — he himself has asserted . . .

Jones. Pugh has sent you mad. You're mad.

Danger-Boy. Sunday morning, Jones. We give you till noon, Jones.

10. THE MOUNTAIN SIDE

(*Caves*)

Thomas. That's today. It's already past noon!

Jones. Yes.

Lily. But it's past mid-day. It's long past . . .

Mark. Why didn't you tell us this before, Jones?

Connie. They won't kill Mr. Pugh, will they? They couldn't . . .

Freda. This is terrible. Let's go and get the water-bottles right away, and fill them up. Jones, we must try . . .

Jones. Freda, it was you who told Mr. Pugh to follow me — you gave him the directions, on the night he became their hostage.

Mark. Why didn't you tell us in time, Jones?

Thomas. We've got to do something before it's too late. My father's up there . . .

Jones. It is too late. He walked into it.

Mark. We should have been consulted, Jones.

Jones. You would have agreed to give them the mineral water.

Mark. Well, rather than let old Pugh . . .

Jones. And that would have been bad.

Mark. But if they drink his blood they are going to be poisoned in any case.

Jones. I mean it would have been bad for us. It's bad to administer poison. Besides, it's against the Geneva . . .

Thomas. I'm going to do something about this.

Connie. So am I. I'll come with you, Thomas.

Jones. It's too late. Listen.

(*Voices from the mountain*)

Freda. There's something going on up there. Look, Lily, come and see. There's a crowd.

Lily. They are coming down. I think they're carrying a man.

Mark. It's the search party. They've found Pugh. Thomas — come back! — you can't do anything. . . .

Jones. Let him go, he'll come back later.

Connie. What a crowd of people! Where are they all coming from? I don't know who . . .

Lily. There's my mother over there. There's Richard Jones helping to carry the man. He's holding the legs.

49

Mark. Simon Rhys holding the other end. And Margiad Rhys . . .

Connie. Freda, I see your uncle in the crowd. My father's there. I suppose he's administered first aid.

Jones. Who else do you see?

Mark. A lot of young people. I don't know who they are. I suppose they were out climbing. They found Mr. Pugh, perhaps . . .

Jones. A *lot* of young people?

Mark. Yes . . . and a lot more. About a hundred at least. Look at those boys — they need a hair-cut. They're coming over the mountain top, in fact. Where have they all come from?

Connie. Listen to the noise! They sound like monkeys.

Freda. Look at them drinking from the stream. . . .

Mark. Here they come, walking down the mountain, Jones. They are following the — Mr. Pugh — the body. It's very white. They are simply walking down the mountain. . . .

Lily. Jones, what shall we do?

Jones. We shall stay here.

11. THE VALLEY

(*Richard's house*)

Ruth. Between ourselves, Danger-Boy — just between you and Richard and me and these four walls — it was getting on time we had a new minister. Not that I had anything against poor Mr. Pugh, and no one would have wished him that end, but he was just a bit lah-di-dah and, well, not like the ministers we used to have.

(*Sound of glasses and bottles being opened*)

Richard. Sucked by the weasels, poor Hughie Pugh. . . .

Ruth. Yes, but Dr. Evans said he must have been lying dead a long time before the weasels got him. Death by misadventure. He must have had an attack, and lost his footing. And then the weasels! There wasn't a drop left in his veins.

Danger-Boy. (*Voice sounds less 'foreign'.*) Do you know, when I saw the body, I seemed to remember his face, but I couldn't quite remember.

Ruth. Oh, he's been all over Wales, preaching. You must have come across Mr. Pugh, he was in all the parishes.

Danger-Boy. Yes, I suppose . . . (*Drinks.*) This is nice stuff.

(*Hums Jones's tune*)

Ruth. It's the best mineral water in the world. Makes you forget your troubles. What's that you're humming, Danger-Boy?

Danger-Boy. I don't know — only a tune I picked up somewhere.

Richard. It takes your mind off things, boy. Drink up.

Ruth. It takes my mind off Lily. Well, it's their choice. If they want to live up there in the mountain there's nothing we can do to prevent it, is there? I mean, you could call in the law, but where would that get you? It would only be a matter of time till they reached the age of twenty-one. I mean, what's the good? I couldn't bear to go through all that again, with Lily sitting mooning up at the mountain all the time. But anyway, now that some of you young people have come to settle here, it's a sort of compensation. I feel I've known you all your life, Danger-Boy.

Richard. You'll get work here. There's plenty of work here for all of you.

Ruth. They'll be off to London, Richard. Just wait — they all go away when the time comes. They want to make their way, Richard. I wish our children had turned out like Danger-Boy and his friends. Listen!

(Sound of song from the mountain)

Danger-Boy. Why are your children living up in the mountain?

Ruth. Richard — the glasses are empty. . . . Well, Danger-Boy, that's what we all want to know. Dr. Evans said, he said to his Connie, 'What's in it?' he said. 'You're only young once,' he said, 'and you're wasting the best years of your lives. You don't have a drink, you don't enjoy yourselves,' he said. 'What do you gain by it?' he said. 'Poverty,' she said — that's what she told her father — 'Poverty, Chastity, Obedience,' she said. 'Well,' he said, 'you won't get fat on that. And you can come home,' he said, 'when you get tired of it.' I can't understand my Lily going in with that lot. It's your boy Jones at the bottom of it, Richard. He's the ringleader. Just listen!

(Sound of song)

Richard. Well, speaking as a bachelor craftsman, I used to believe, when I was young, that an abstemious life was necessary to the craftsman. But it doesn't get you anywhere. Do you see that cabinet over there, Danger-Boy? Beautifully inlaid, a lovely bit of timber.

Danger-Boy. It looks nice. (*Whistles tune while eyeing the cabinet.*)

Richard. Well, it was rejected by the Eisteddfod committee for woodwork. Not functional enough in the design. So drink up and forget your troubles.

Danger-Boy. All the best.

Ruth. Do you know, Danger-Boy, it's only a few weeks that you young people have been here, but your eyes are beginning to open, they aren't narrow slits any more. And your voices are changing, too. When you first came down here we couldn't decide what you were — Germans, Poles, Czechs . . .

Richard. Chinese, Croats . . .

Ruth. Serbs, Russians, Icelanders. But you're getting to be like us. What was it like over the other side of the mountain, Danger-Boy?

Danger-Boy. A bit dangerous. . . .

Ruth. Dangerous? I never heard it was very steep on that side.

Danger-Boy. Well, I say 'dangerous.' . . . I don't know. It was a hard life, I think. I don't remember, really.

Richard. Drink up, Danger-Boy. You'll soon forget your troubles, you'll forget them.

Ruth. Listen!

(*Sound of song from the mountain*)

The Ormolu Clock

THE Hotel Stroh stood side by side with the Guest-house Lublonitsch, separated by a narrow path that led up the mountain, on the Austrian side, to the Yugoslavian border. Perhaps the old place had once been a great hunting tavern. These days, though, the Hotel Stroh was plainly a disappointment to its few drooping tenants. They huddled together like birds in a storm; their flesh sagged over the unscrubbed tables on the dark back veranda, which looked over Herr Stroh's untended fields. Usually, Herr Stroh sat somewhat apart, in a mist of cognac, his lower chin resting on his red neck, and his shirt open for air. Those visitors who had come not for the climbing but simply for the view sat and admired the mountain and were sloppily waited upon until the weekly bus should come and carry them away. If they had cars, they rarely stayed long — they departed, as a rule, within two hours of arrival, like a comic act. This much was entertainingly visible from the other side of the path, at the Guesthouse Lub-lonitsch.

I was waiting for friends to come and pick me up on their way to Venice. Frau Lublonitsch welcomed all her guests in person. When I arrived I was hardly aware of the honour, she seemed so merely a local

54

woman — undefined and dumpy as she emerged from the kitchen wiping her hands on her brown apron, with her grey hair drawn back tight, her sleeves rolled up, her dingy dress, black stockings, and boots. It was only gradually that her importance was permitted to dawn upon strangers.

There was a Herr Lublonitsch, but he was of no account, even though he got all the martial courtesies. He sat punily with his drinking friends at one of the tables in front of the inn, greeting the guests as they passed in and out and receiving as much attention as he wanted from the waitresses. When he was sick Frau Lublonitsch took his meals with her own hands to a room upstairs set aside for his sickness. But she was undoubtedly the boss.

She worked the hired girls fourteen hours a day, and they did the work cheerfully. She was never heard to complain or to give an order; it was enough that she was there. Once, when a girl dropped a tray with five mugs of soup, Frau Lublonitsch went and fetched a cloth and submissively mopped up the mess herself, like any old peasant who had suffered worse than that in her time. The maids called her Frau Chef. 'Frau Chef prepares special food when her husband's stomach is bad,' one of them told me.

Appended to the guesthouse was a butcher's shop, and this was also a Lublonitsch possession. A grocer's shop had been placed beside it, and on an adjacent plot of ground — all Lublonitsch property — a draper's shop was nearing completion. Two of her sons worked in the butcher's establishment; a third had been placed in charge of the grocer's; and the youngest son, now ready to take his place, was destined for the draper's.

55

In the garden, strangely standing on a path between the flowers for decorating the guests' tables and the vegetables for eating, facing the prolific orchard and overhung by the chestnut trees that provided a roof for outdoor diners, grew one useless thing — a small, well-tended palm tree. It gave an air to the place. Small as it was, this alien plant stood as high as the distant mountain peaks when seen from the perspective of the great back porch where we dined. It quietly dominated the view.

Ordinarily, I got up at seven, but one morning I woke at half past five and came down from my room on the second floor to the yard, to find someone to make me some coffee. Standing in the sunlight, with her back to me, was Frau Lublonitsch. She was regarding her wide kitchen garden, her fields beyond it, her outbuildings and her pigsties where two aged women were already at work. One of the sons emerged from an outbuilding carrying several strings of long sausages. Another led a bullock with a bag tied over its head to a tree and chained it there to await the slaughterers. Frau Lublonitsch did not move but continued to survey her property, her pigs, her pig-women, her chestnut trees, her beanstalks, her sausages, her sons, her tall gladioli, and — as if she had eyes in the back of her head — she seemed aware, too, of the good thriving guesthouse behind her, and the butcher's shop, the draper's shop, and the grocer's.

Just as she turned to attack the day's work, I saw that she glanced at the sorry Hotel Stroh across the path. I saw her mouth turn down at the corners with the amusement of one who has a certain foreknowledge;

I saw a landowner's recognition in her little black eyes.

You could tell, even before the local people told you, that Frau Lublonitsch had built up the whole thing from nothing by her own wits and industry. But she worked pitiably hard. She did all the cooking. She supervised the household, and, without moving hurriedly, she sped into the running of the establishment like the maniac drivers from Vienna who tore along the highroad in front of her place. She scoured the huge pans herself, wielding her podgy arm round and round; clearly, she trusted none of the girls to do the job properly. She was not above sweeping the floor, feeding the pigs, and serving in the butcher's shop, where she would patiently hold one after another great sausage under her customer's nose for him to smell its quality. She did not sit down, except to take her dinner in the kitchen, from her rising at dawn to her retiring at one in the morning.

Why does she do it, what for? Her sons are grown up, she's got her guesthouse, her servants, her shops, her pigs, fields, cattle——

At the café across the river, where I went in the late afternoon, they said, 'Frau Lublonitsch has got far more than that. She owns all the strip of land up to the mountain. She's got three farms. She may even expand across the river and down this way to the town.'

'Why does she work so hard? She dresses like a peasant,' they said. 'She scours the pots.' Frau Lublonitsch was their favourite subject.

She did not go to church, she was above church. I had hoped to see her there, wearing different clothes and perhaps sitting with the chemist, the dentist, and their wives in the second-front row behind the count and his family; or perhaps she might have taken some less noticeable place among the congregation. But Frau Lublonitsch was a church unto herself, and even resembled in shape the onion-shaped spires of the churches around her.

I climbed the lower slopes of the mountains while the experts in their boots did the thing earnestly up on the sheer crags above the clouds. When it rained, they came back and reported, 'Tito is sending the bad weather.' The maids were bored with the joke, but they obliged with smiles every time, and served them up along with the interminable veal.

The higher mountain reaches were beyond me except by bus. I was anxious, however, to scale the peaks of Frau Lublonitsch's nature.

One morning, when everything was glittering madly after a nervous stormy night, I came down early to look for coffee. I had heard voices in the yard some moments before, but by the time I appeared they had gone indoors. I followed the voices to the dark stone kitchen and peered in the doorway. Beyond the chattering girls, I caught sight of a further doorway, which usually remained closed. Now it was open.

Within it was a bedroom reaching far back into the house. It was imperially magnificent. It was done in red and gold. I saw a canopied bed, built high, splendidly covered with a scarlet quilt. The pillows were piled up at the head — about four of them, very white. The bed head was deep dark wood, touched with gilt.

58

A golden fringe hung from the canopy. In some ways this bed reminded me of the glowing bed by which van Eyck ennobled the portrait of Jan Arnolfini and his wife. All the rest of the Lublonitsch establishment was scrubbed and polished local wood, but this was a very poetic bed.

The floor of the bedroom was covered with a carpet of red which was probably crimson but which, against the scarlet of the bed, looked purple. On the walls on either side of the bed hung Turkish carpets whose background was an opulently dull, more ancient red — almost black where the canopy cast its shade.

I was moved by the sight. The girl called Mitzi was watching me as I stood in the kitchen doorway. 'Coffee?' she said.

'Whose room is that?'

'It's Frau Chef's room. She sleeps there.'

Now another girl, tall, lanky Gertha, with her humorous face and slightly comic answer to everything, skipped over to the bedroom door and said, 'We are instructed to keep the door closed,' and for a moment before closing it she drew open the door quite wide for me to see some more of the room. I caught sight of a tiled stove constructed of mosaic tiles that were not a local type; they were lustrous — ochre and green — resembling the tiles on the floors of Byzantine ruins. The stove looked like a temple. I saw a black lacquered cabinet inlaid with mother-of-pearl, and just before Gertha closed the door I noticed, standing upon the cabinet, a large ornamental clock, its case enamelled rosily with miniature inset pastel paintings; each curve and twirl in the case of this clock was overlaid with that gilded-bronze alloy which is known as ormolu. The clock twinkled in the early sunlight which slanted between the window hangings.

I went into the polished dining-room, and Mitzi brought my coffee there. From the window I could see Frau Lublonitsch in her dark dress, her black boots and wool stockings. She was plucking a chicken over a bucketful of feathers. Beyond her I could see the sulky figure of Herr Stroh standing collarless, fat and unshaven, in the open door of his hotel across the path. He seemed to be meditating upon Frau Lublonitsch.

It was that very day that the nuisance occurred. The double windows of my bedroom were directly opposite the bedroom windows of the Hotel Stroh, with no more than twenty feet between — the width of the narrow path that led up to the frontier.

It was a cold day. I sat in my room writing letters. I glanced out of the window. In the window directly opposite me stood Herr Stroh, gazing blatantly upon me. I was annoyed at his interest. I pulled down the blind and switched on the light to continue my writing. I wondered if Herr Stroh had seen me doing anything peculiar before I had noticed him, such as tapping my head with the end of my pen or scratching my nose or pulling at my chin, or one of the things one might do while writing a letter. The drawn blind and the artificial light irritated me, and suddenly I didn't see why I shouldn't write my letters by daylight without being stared at. I switched off the light and released the blind. Herr Stroh had gone. I concluded that he had taken my action as a signal of disapproval, and I settled back to write.

I looked up a few moments later, and this time Herr Stroh was seated on a chair a little way back from the window. He was facing me squarely and holding to his eyes a pair of field-glasses.

I left my room and went down to complain to Frau Lublonitsch.

'She's gone to the market,' Gertha said. 'She'll be back in half an hour.'

So I lodged my complaint with Gertha.

'I shall tell Frau Chef,' she said.

Something in her manner made me ask, 'Has this ever happened before?'

'Once or twice this year,' she said. 'I'll speak to Frau Chef.' And she added, with her music-hall grimace, 'He was probably counting your eyelashes.'

I returned to my room. Herr Stroh still sat in position, the field-glasses in his hands resting on his knees. As soon as I came within view, he raised the glasses to his eyes. I decided to stare him out until such time as Frau Lublonitsch should return and take the matter in hand.

For nearly an hour I sat patiently at the window. Herr Stroh rested his arms now and again, but he did not leave his seat. I could see him clearly, although I think I imagined the grin on his face as, from time to time, he raised the glasses to his eyes. There was no doubt that he could see, as if it were within an inch of his face, the fury on mine. It was too late now for one of us to give in, and I kept glancing down at the entrances to the Hotel Stroh, expecting to see Frau Lublonitsch or perhaps one of her sons or the yard hands going across to deliver a protest. But no one from our side approached the Stroh premises, from either the front or the back of the house. I continued to stare, and Herr Stroh continued to goggle through his glasses.

Then he dropped them. It was as if they had been jerked out of his hands by an invisible nudge. He approached close to the window and gazed, but now he was gazing at a point above and slightly to the left of my room. After about two minutes, he turned and disappeared.

Just then Gertha knocked at my door. 'Frau Chef has protested, and you won't have any more trouble,' she said.

'Did she telephone to his house?'

'No, Frau Chef doesn't use the phone; it mixes her up.'

'Who protested, then?'

'Frau Chef.'

'But she hasn't been across to see him. I've been watching the house.'

'No, Frau Chef doesn't visit with him. But don't worry, he knows all right that he mustn't annoy our guests.'

When I looked out of the window again, I saw that the blind of Herr Stroh's room had been pulled down, and so it remained for the rest of my stay.

Meantime, I went out to post my letters in the box opposite our hotel, across the path. The sun had come out more strongly, and Herr Stroh stood in his doorway blinking up at the roof of the Guesthouse Lublonitsch. He was engrossed, he did not notice me at all.

I didn't want to draw his attention by following the line of his gaze but I was curious as to what held him staring so trancelike up at our roof. On my way back from the postbox I saw what it was.

Like most of the roofs in that province, the Lublonitsch roof had a railed ledge running several inches
above the eaves, for the purpose of preventing the snow
from falling in heavy thumps during the winter. On
this ledge, just below an attic window, stood the gold-
and-rose ormolu clock that I had seen in Frau Lublonitsch's splendid bedroom.

I turned the corner just as Herr Stroh gave up his
gazing; he went indoors, sullen and bent. Two car-
loads of people who had moved into the hotel that
morning were now moving out, shifting their baggage
with speed and the signs of a glad departure. I knew
that his house was nearly empty.

Before supper, I walked past the Hotel Stroh and
down across the bridge to the café. There were no
other customers in the place. The proprietor brought
the harsh gin that was the local speciality over to my
usual table and I sipped it while I waited for someone
to come. I did not have to wait long, for two local
women came in and ordered ices, as many of them did
on their way home from work in the village shops.
They held the long spoons in their rough, knobbly
hands and talked, while the owner of the café came and
sat with them to exchange the news of the day.

'Herr Stroh has been defying Frau Lublonitsch,' one
of the women said.

'Not again?'

'He's been offending her tourists.'

'Dirty old Peeping Tom.'

'He only does it to annoy Frau Lublonitsch.'

'I saw the clock on the roof. I saw——'

'Stroh is finished, he——'

'Which clock?'

'What she bought from him last winter when he was hard up. All red and gold, like an altarpiece. A beautiful clock — it was his grandfather's when things were different.'

'Stroh is finished. She'll have his hotel. She'll have——'

'She'll have the pants off him.'

'He'll have to go. She'll get the place at her price. Then she'll build down to the bridge. Just wait and see. Next winter she'll have the Hotel Stroh. Last winter she had the clock. It's two years since she gave him the mortgage.'

'It's only Stroh's place that's standing in her way. She'll pull it down.'

The faces of the two women and the man nearly met across the café table, hypnotised by the central idea of their talk. The women's spoons rose to their mouths and returned to their ices while the man clasped his hands on the table in front of him. Their voices went on like a litany.

'She'll expand down to the bridge.'

'Perhaps beyond the bridge.'

'No, no, the bridge will be enough. She's not so young.'

'Poor old Stroh!'

'Why doesn't she expand in the other direction?'

'Because there isn't so much trade in the other direction.'

'The business is down here, this side of the river.'

'Old Stroh is upset.'

'She'll build down to the bridge. She'll pull down his place and build.'

'Beyond the bridge.'

'Old Stroh. His clock stuck up there for everyone to see.'

'What does he expect, the lazy old pig?'

'What does he expect to see with his field-glasses?'

'The tourists.'

'I wish him joy of the tourists.'

They giggled, then noticed me sitting within earshot, and came out of their trance.

How delicately Frau Lublonitsch had sent her deadly message! The ormolu clock was still there on the roof ledge when I returned. It was thus she had told him that time was passing and the end of summer was near, and that his hotel, like his clock, would soon be hers. As I passed, Herr Stroh shuffled out to his front door, rather drunk. He did not see me. He was looking at the clock where it hung in the sunset, he looked up at it as did the quaking enemies of the Lord upon the head of Holofernes. I wondered if the poor man would even live another winter; certainly he had taken his last feeble stand against Frau Lublonitsch.

As for her, she would probably live till she was ninety or more. The general estimate of her age was fifty-three, fifty-four, five, six: a healthy woman.

Next day, the clock was gone. Enough was enough. It had gone back to that glamorous room behind the kitchen to which Frau Lublonitsch retired in the early hours of the morning to think up her high conceptions, not lying supine like a defeated creature but propped up on the white pillows, surrounded by her crimson, her scarlet, her gold-and-rosy tints, which, like a religious discipline, disturbed her spirit out of its sloth. It was from here she planted the palm tree and built the shops.

When, next morning, I saw her scouring the pots in the yard and plodding about in her boots among the vegetables, I was somewhat terrified. She could have adorned her own person in scarlet and gold, she could have lived in a turreted mansion rivalling that of the apothecary in the village. But like one averting the evil eye, or like one practising a pure disinterested art, she had stuck to her brown apron and her boots. And she would, without a doubt, have her reward. She would take the Hotel Stroh. She would march on the bridge, and beyond it. The café would be hers, the swimming pool, the cinema. All the market place would be hers before she died in the scarlet bed under the gold-fringed canopy, facing her ormolu clock, her deed boxes, and her ineffectual bottle of medicine.

Almost as if they knew it, the three tourists remaining in the Hotel Stroh came over to inquire of Frau Lublonitsch if there were any rooms available and what her terms were. Her terms were modest, and she found room for two of them. The third left on his motorcycle that night.

Everyone likes to be on the winning side. I saw the two new arrivals from the Hotel Stroh sitting secure under the Lublonitsch chestnut trees, taking breakfast, next morning. Herr Stroh, more sober than before, stood watching the scene from his doorway. I thought, Why doesn't he spit on us, he's got nothing to lose? I saw again, in my mind's eye, the ormolu clock set high in the sunset splendour. But I had not yet got over my fury with him for spying into my room, and was moved, all in one stroke, with high contempt and deep pity, feverish triumph and chilly fear.

The Curtain Blown by the Breeze

IT is always when a curtain at an open window
flutters in the breeze that I think of that frail white
curtain, a piece of fine gauze, which was drawn
across the bedroom windows of Mrs. Van der Merwe.
I never saw the original curtains, which were so care-
lessly arranged as to leave a gap through which that
picannin of twelve had peeped, one night three years
before, and had watched Mrs. Van der Merwe suckle
her child, and been caught and shot dead by Jannie,
her husband. The original curtains had now been replaced by this more delicate stuff, and the husband's
sentence still had five years to run, and meanwhile Mrs.
Van der Merwe was changing her character.

She stopped slouching; she lost the lanky, sullen look
of a smallholder's wife; she cleared the old petrol cans
out of the yard, and that was only a start; she became a
tall lighthouse sending out kindly beams which some
took for welcome instead of warnings against the rocks.
She bought the best china, stopped keeping pound notes
stuffed in a stocking, called herself Sonia instead of
Sonji, and entertained.

This was a territory where you could not bathe in
the gentlest stream but a germ from the water entered
your kidneys and blighted your body for life; where

you could not go for a walk before six in the evening without returning crazed by the sun; and in this remote part of the territory, largely occupied by poor whites amidst the overwhelming natural growth of natives, a young spinster could not keep a cat for a pet but it would be one day captured and pitifully shaved by the local white bachelors for fun; it was a place where the tall grass was dangerous from snakes and the floors dangerous from scorpions. The white people seized on the slightest word, Nature took the lightest footfall, with fanatical seriousness. The English nurses discovered that they could not sit next a man at dinner and be agreeable — perhaps asking him, so as to slice up the boredom, to tell them all the story of his life — without his taking it for a great flirtation and turning up next day after breakfast for the love affair; it was a place where there was never a breath of breeze except in the season of storms and where the curtains in the windows never moved in the breeze unless a storm was to follow.

The English nurses were often advised to put in for transfers to another district.

'It's so much brighter in the north. Towns, life. Civilisation, shops. Much cooler — you see, it's high up there in the north. The races.'

'You would like it in the east — those orange planters. Everything is greener, there's a huge valley. Shooting.'

'Why did they send you nurses to this unhealthy spot? You should go to a healthy spot.'

Some of the nurses left Fort Beit. But those of us who were doing tropical diseases had to stay on, because our clinic, the largest in the Colony, was also a research centre for tropical diseases. Those of us who had to stay on used sometimes to say to each other, 'Isn't it wonderful here? Heaps of servants. Cheap drinks. Birds, beasts, flowers.'

The place was not without its strange marvels. I never got used to its travel-film colours except in the dry season when the dust made everything real. The dust was thick in the great yard behind the clinic where the natives squatted and stood about, shouting or laughing — it came to the same thing — cooking and eating, while they awaited treatment, or the results of X-rays, or the results of an X-ray of a distant relative. They gave off a fierce smell and kicked up the dust. The sore eyes of the babies were always beset by flies, but the babies slept on regardless, slung on their mothers' backs, and when they woke and cried the women suckled them.

The poor whites of Fort Beit and its area had a reception room of their own inside the building, and here they ate the food they had brought, and lolled about in long silences, sometimes working up to a fight in a corner. The remainder of the society of Fort Beit did not visit the clinic.

The remainder comprised the chemist, the clergyman, the veterinary surgeon, the police and their families. These enjoyed a social life of a small and remote quality, only coming into contact with the poor white small-farmers for business purposes. They were anxious to entertain the clinic staff who mostly spent its free time elsewhere — miles and miles away, driving at weekends to the capital, the north, or to one of the big dams on which it was possible to set up for a sailor. But sometimes the nurses and medical officers would, for a change, spend an evening in the village at the house of the chemist, the clergyman, the vet, or at the police quarters.

Into this society came Sonia Van der Merwe when her husband had been three years in prison. There was a certain slur attached to his sentence since it was generally felt he had gone too far in the heat of the moment, this sort of thing undermining the prestige of the Colony at Whitehall. But nobody held the incident against Sonia. The main difficulty she had to face in her efforts towards the company of the vet, the chemist and the clergyman was the fact that she had never yet been in their company.

The Van der Merwes' farm lay a few miles outside Fort Beit. It was one of the few farms in the district, for this was an area which had only been developed for the mines, and these had lately closed down. The Van der Merwes had lived the makeshift, toiling lives of Afrikaans settlers who had trekked up from the Union. I do not think it had ever before occurred to Sonia that her days could be spent otherwise than in rising and washing her face at the tub outside, baking bread, scrappily feeding her children, yelling at the natives, and retiring at night to her feather bed with Jannie. Her only outings had been to the Dutch Reformed gathering at Easter when the Afrikaans came in along the main street in their covered wagons and settled there for a week.

It was not till the lawyer came to arrange some affair between the farm and the Land Bank that she learned she could actually handle the fortune her father had left her, for she had imagined that only the pound notes she kept stuffed in the stocking were of real spending worth; her father in his time had never spent his money on visible things, but had invested it, and Sonia thought that money paid into the bank was a sort of tribute-money to the bank people which patriarchal farmers like her father were obliged to pay under the strict ethic of the Dutch Reformed Church. She now understood her cash value, and felt fiercely against her husband for failing to reveal it to her. She wrote a letter to him, which was a difficult course. I saw the final draft, about which she called a conference of nurses from the clinic. We were wicked enough to let it go, but in fact I don't think we gave it much thought. I recall that on this occasion we talked far into the night about her possibilities — her tennis court, her two bathrooms, her black-and-white bedroom — all of which were as yet only a glimmer at the end of a tunnel. In any case, I do not think we could have succeeded in changing her mind about the letter which subsequently enjoyed a few inches in the local press as part of Jannie's evidence. It was as follows:

Dear Jannie there is going to be some changes I found out what pa left is cash to spend I only got to sine my name do you think I like to go on like this work work work counting the mealies in the field By God like poor whites when did I get a dress you did not say a word that is your shame and you have landed in jale with your bad temper you shoud of amed at the legs. Mr. Little came here to bring the papers to sine he said you get good cooking in jale the kids are well but Hannah got a bite but I will take them away from there now and send them to the convent and pay money. Your Loving Wife, S. Van der Merwe

There must have been many occasions on which I lay on my bed on summer afternoons in Worcestershire, because at that time I was convalescent. My school-days had come to an end. My training as a radio-therapist was not to begin till the autumn.

I do not know how many afternoons I lay on my bed listening to a litany of tennis noises from where my two brothers played on the court a little to the right below my window. Sometimes, to tell me it was time to get up, my elder brother Richard would send a tennis ball through the open window. The net curtain would stir and part very suddenly and somewhere in the room the ball would thud and then roll. I always thought one day he would break the glass of the window, or that he would land the ball on my face or break something in the room, but he never did. Perhaps my memory exaggerates the number of these occasions and really they only occurred once or twice.

But I am sure the curtains must have moved in the breeze as I lay taking in the calls and the to and fro of tennis on those unconcerned afternoons, and I suppose the sight was a pleasurable one. That a slight move-ment of the curtains should be the sign of a summer breeze seems somewhere near to truth, for to me truth has airy properties with buoyant and lyrical effects; and when anything drastic starts up from some light cause it only proves to me that something false has got into the world.

I do not actually remember the curtains of my room being touched by the summer wind although I am sure they were; whenever I try to bring to mind this detail of the afternoon sensations it disappears, and I have knowledge of the image only as one who has swallowed some fruit of the Tree of Knowledge — its memory is usurped by the window of Mrs. Van der Merwe's house and by the curtains disturbed, in the rainy season, by a trifling wind, unreasonably meaning a storm.

Sometimes, on those restful afternoons, I was anxious. There was some doubt about my acceptance for training as a radio-therapist because of my interrupted schooling. One day the letter of acceptance came by the late post. I read the letter with relief and delight, and at that same moment decided to turn down the offer. It was enough that I had received it. I am given to this sort of thing, and the reason that I am drawn to moderate and tranquil motives is that I lack them. I decided instead to become a hospital nurse and later to follow my brother Richard, who was then a medical student, to Africa, and specialise, with him, in tropical diseases.

It was about a year after my arrival at Fort Beit that I came across Sonji Van der Merwe and, together with the other nurses, read the letter which was about to be sent to her husband four hundred miles away in the Colony's prison. She posted the letter ritualistically the next afternoon, putting on her church-going gloves to do so. She did not expect, nor did she receive, a reply. Three weeks later she started calling herself Sonia.

Our visits to the farm began to take the place of evenings spent at the vet's, the chemist's and the clergyman's, to whose society Sonia now had good hopes of access. And every time we turned up something new had taken place. Sonia knew, or discovered as if by bush-telegraph, where to begin. She did not yet know how to travel by train and would have been afraid to make any excursion by herself far from the area, but through one nurse or another she obtained furnishings from the Union, catalogues, books about interior decoration and fashion magazines. Travel-stained furniture vans began to arrive at her bidding and our instigation. Her first move, however, was to join the Church of England, abandoning the Dutch Reformed persuasion of her forefathers; we had to hand it to her that she had thought this up for herself.

We egged her on from week to week. We taught her how not to be mean with her drinks, for she had ordered an exotic supply. At first she had locked the bottles in the pantry and poured them into glasses in the kitchen and watered them before getting the house boy to serve them to her guests. We stopped all that. A contractor already had the extensions to the house in hand, and the rooms were being decorated and furnished one by one. It was I who had told her to have two bathrooms, not merely one, installed. She took time getting used to the indoor lavatories and we had to keep reminding her to pull the chain. One of us brought back from the capital a book of etiquette which was twenty-eight years old but which she read assiduously, following the words with her forefinger. I think it was I who had suggested the black-and-white bedroom, being a bit drunk at the time, and now it was a wonder to see it taking shape; it was done within a month — she had managed to obtain black wallpaper, and to put it up, although wallpaper was a thing unheard of in the Colony and she was warned by everyone that it would never stick to the walls. There was in this bedroom a white carpet and a chaise-longue covered with black-and-white candy-striped satin. It was less than a year before she got round to adding the Beardsley reproductions, but by that time she was entertaining, and had the benefit of the vet's counsel, he having once been a young man in London.

She told us one day — lying on the chaise-longue and looking very dramatic with her lanky hair newly piled up and her black chiffon dressing-gown — the story of the picannin, which we already knew:

'It was through that window he was looking. Yere I was sitting yere on the bed feeding the baby and I look up at the window and so help me God it was a blerry nig standing outside with his face at the window. You should of heard me scream. So Jannie got the gun and caught the pic and I hear the bang. So he went too far in his blerry temper so what can you expect? Now I won't have no more trouble from them boys. That's the very window, I was careless to leave the curtain aside. So we show them what's what and we get a new set of boys. We didn't have no boys on the farm, they all run away.'

There was a slight warm breeze floating in little gusts through the window. 'We'd better be getting back,' said one of the girls. 'There's going to be a storm.'

A storm in the Colony was such that before it broke the whole place was spasmodic like an exposed nerve, and after it was over the body of the world from horizon to horizon moved in a slow daze back into its place. Before it broke there was the little wind, then a pearly light, then an earthen smell; the birds screamed and suddenly stopped, and the insects disappeared. Afterwards the flying ants wriggled in a drugged condition out of the cracks in the walls, found their wings, and flew off in crazy directions, the more extreme colours of the storm faded out of the sky in a defeated sort of way, and the furniture felt clammy from the ordeal. One day I was caught at Sonia's house when a storm broke. This was when she had already settled in to her status, and the extensions to the house were completed, and the furniture all in place. Night fell soon after the storm was over, and we sat in her very Europeanised drawing-room — for she had done away with the stoep — sipping pink gins; the drinks were served by a native with huge ape-like hands clutching the tray, his hands emerging from the cuffs of the green-and-white uniform which had lately glared in the light of the storm. Sonia kept saying, 'I feel I've made a corner of civilisation for myself in doing up this house.' It was a version of one of the clergyman's chance compliments on one of his visits; she had seized on it as a verity, and made it known to all her visitors. 'I feel I must live up to it, man,' she said. I was always amazed at her rapid acquisition of new words and highly useful sayings.

Outside, the night sounds were coming back. One could hear the beasts finding each other again by their calls whenever Sonia stopped talking, and even further in the distance, the drum business, with news of which kraals had been swamped and wrecked, or perhaps no news, for all we understood of their purpose. Just outside the window there was an occasional squelch of bare feet on the wet gravel drive which Sonia had constructed. She rose and adjusted the light window curtains, then drew the big ones. She was better now. During the storm she had squatted with hunched shoulders on the carpet like a native in his hut, letting

76

the waves of sound and light break over her. It was generally thought she had some coloured blood. But this, now that she had begun to reveal such visible proof of her glamorous fortune and character, was no bar to the society of the vet, the chemist and the clergyman. Many of the doctors from the clinic visited her and were enchanted by her eccentric grandeur, and much preferred her company to that of the tropical-skinned vet's wife and the watery blonde chemist's wife and the music-loving clergyman's wife, at sultry sundowner times in the rainy season. My brother Richard was fascinated by Sonia.

We nurses were astonished that the men were so dazzled. She was our creature, our folly, our lark. We had lavished our imagination upon her eager mind and had ourselves designed the long voile 'afternoon' dresses, and had ourselves put it to her that she must have a path leading down to the river and a punt on the little river and a pink parasol to go with the punt. There was something in the air of the place that affected the men, even those newly out from England, with an overturn of discrimination. One of the research workers at the clinic had already married a brassy barmaid from Johannesburg, another had married a neurotic dressmaker from the Cape who seemed to have dozens of elbows, so much did she throw her long bony arms about. We too were subject to the influence of the place but we did not think of this when we were engrossed in our bizarre cultivation of Sonia and our dressing her up to kill. At the time, we only saw the men taking our fantasy in earnest, and looked at each other, smiled and looked away.

77

In the year before Jannie Van der Merwe was due to be released from prison I spent much of my free time at Sonia's with my brother Richard. Her house was by now a general meeting-place for the district and she conducted quite a salon every late afternoon. About this time I became engaged to marry a research worker at the clinic.

I do not know if Richard slept with Sonia. He was very enamoured of her and would not let anyone make fun of her in his hearing.

She said one day: 'Why d'you want to marry that Frank? Man, he looks like your brother, you want to catch a fellow that doesn't look like one of the family. I could get you a fellow more your type.'

I was irritated by this. I kept Frank from seeing her as much as possible; but it was not possible; all our lives outside the clinic seemed to revolve round Sonia. When Frank began to ridicule Sonia I knew he was in some way, which he was afraid to admit, attracted by her.

She chattered incessantly, her voice accented in the Afrikaans way. I had to admire her quick grasp of every situation, for now she was acquainted with the inner politics of the clinic, and managed to put in effective words here and there with visiting Government officials who took it for granted she had ruled the district for years and, being above the common run, pleased herself how she dressed and what she did.

I heard her discussing our disagreeable chief radiologist with an important member of the Medical Board: 'Man, he got high spirits I tell you, man. I see him dig the spurs into the horse when he pass my house every morning, he goes riding to work off those high spirits. But I tell you one thing, he's good at his job. Man,

78

he's first rate at the job.' Soon after this our ill-tempered radiologist, who did not ride very frequently, was transferred to another district. It was only when I heard that the important man from the Medical Board was a fanatical horse-lover that I realised the full force of Sonia's abilities.

'God, what have we done?' I said to my best friend.

She said, 'Leave well alone. She's getting us a new wing.'

Sonia made plans to obtain for Richard the job of Chief Medical Officer in the north. I suspected that Sonia meant to follow him to the north if he should be established there, for she had remarked one day that she would have to get used to travel; it must be easy: 'Man, everyone does it. Drink up. Cheerio.'

Frank had also applied for the job. He said — looking at the distance with his short-sighted eyes, which gave to his utterances a suggestion of disinterestedness — 'I've got better qualifications for it than Richard.' So he had. 'Richard is the better research worker,' Frank said. This was true. 'Richard should stay here and I should go up north,' Frank said. 'You would like it up there,' he said. All this was undeniable.

It became apparent very soon that Frank was competing with Richard for Sonia's attention. He did this without appearing to notice it himself, as if it were some routine performance in the clinic, not the method but the results of which interested him. I could hardly believe the ridiculous carry-on of these two men.

'Do they think she will really have any influence in the question of that job?'

'Yes,' my best friend said, 'and so she will.'

That important member of the Medical Board — he who was passionate about horses — was in the district again. He had come for a long week-end's fishing. It was all mad. There was no big fishing at Fort Beit.

I began to want Richard to get the job. I cooled off where Frank was concerned; he did not notice, but I cooled off. Richard had become highly nervous. As soon as he had free time he raced off in his car to Sonia's. Frank, who was less scrupulous about taking free time, was usually there first.

I was at the tea-party when the ageing, loose-mouthed, keen-eyed chief of the Medical Board turned up. Richard and Frank sat at opposite ends of a sofa. Richard looked embarrassed; I knew he was thinking of the job, and trying not to seem to be exploiting his attachment to Sonia. I sat near them. Sonia, reciting a long formula from her book of etiquette, introduced us to the important man. As she did so it struck me that this recitation might to some ears sound like a charming gesture against the encroaching slackness of the times. She sat the man between Richard and Frank, and clearly she meant business.

She stood by. She had a beautiful shape; we nurses had not provided that, we had only called it forth from the peasant slouch. She said to the old man, 'Richard yere wants to talk to you, Basil, man,' and touched Richard's shoulder. Frank was peering into the abstract distance. It occurred to me that Frank was the administrative type; none of the research workers I had known were dispassionate, they were vulnerable and nervous.

Richard was nervous. He did not look at the man,

he was looking up at Sonia's face with its West-End make-up.

'Applied for the job up north?' said this Basil to Richard.

'Yes,' Richard said, and smiled with relief.

'Want it?' said the man, casually, in his great importance.

'Oh, rather,' Richard said.

'Well, have it,' said the man, flicking away the invisible job with his forefinger as lightly as if it were a ping-pong ball.

'Well,' Richard said, 'no thank you.'

'What did you say?' said the man.

'What that you say?' said Sonia.

My brother and I are very unlike in most ways, but there are a few radical points of similarity between us. It must be something in the blood.

'No thank you,' Richard was saying. 'After all, I feel I ought to go on with research in tropical diseases.'

Sonia's fury only made a passing pattern on her face. Her first thought was for the old man, fussed and suddenly groundless as he was. 'Basil, man,' she said, bending over him with her breasts about his ears, 'you got the wrong chap. This yere Frank is the boy I was talking of to you. Frank, may I have the honour to introduce to you this yere distinguished——'

'Yes, we've met,' said the man, turning to Frank.

Frank returned from the middle distance. 'I've applied for the job,' he said, 'and my qualifications are, I think——'

'Married?'

'No, but hoping to be.' He turned duly to me and I smiled back most nastily.

'Want the job?'

'Oh, rather.'

'Sure?'

'Oh yes, quite sure.'

The old man was not going to be caught again. 'I hope you really want the job. There are a good many excellent applicants and we want a keen——'

'Yes, I want the job.'

Sonia said, 'Well, have it,' and I thought, then, she had really done for the whole thing and outrun her influence.

But the old man beamed up at her, took both her prettily-restored hands in his, and I nearly saw his slack mouth water.

Other people were pressing round for a word with this Medical Board man. Sonia was treating Richard with ostentatious neglect. Frank was leaning against the wall, now, talking to her. Suddenly I did not want to lose Frank. I looked round the company and wondered what I was doing there, and said to Richard, 'Let's go.'

Richard was looking at Sonia's back. 'Why do you want to go?' Richard said. 'It's early yet. Why?'

Because the curtain was fluttering at the open window, letting in wafts of the savage territory beyond the absurd drawing-room. The people were getting excited; I thought soon they might scream, once or twice like the birds, and then be silent. I thought, even, that Richard might change his mind again about the job, and tell Sonia so, and leave it to her to sort it out for him. It was the pull of Sonia that made him reluctant to leave. She was adjusting Frank's tie and telling him he needed looking after, for all the world as if she had been brought up to that old line; we must tell her, I thought, not to do that sort of thing in public. And I would gladly have stayed on till sundowner time in order to jerk Frank back into a sense of my personality; but there was a storm coming, and it was no fun driving home through a storm.

Richard is stronger-willed than I am. After this party he kept away from Sonia's and stuck in to his work. I broke off my engagement. It was impossible to know whether Frank was relieved or not. There were still three months before he was to take up his appointment in the north. He spent most of his time with Sonia. I was not sure how things stood between them. I still drove over to Sonia's sometimes and found Frank there. I was dissatisfied and attracted by both of them and by their situation. In the dry spells they would often be down the river in the punt when I arrived, and I would wait for the sight of the returning pink parasol, and be glad of the sight. Once or twice when we met at the clinic Frank said to me, factually, 'We could still be married.' Once he said, 'Old Sonia's only a joke, you know.' But I thought he was afraid I might take him at his word, or might do so too soon.

Sonia spoke again of travelling. She was learning to study road maps. She told one of the nurses, 'When Frank's settled up at the north I'll go up and settle him down nicer.' She told another of the nurses, 'My old husband's coming from gaol this month, next month, I don't know, man. He'll see some changes. He get used to them.'

One afternoon I drove over to the farm; I had not seen Sonia for six weeks because her children had been home for the holidays and I loathed her children. I had missed her, she was never boring. The house boy said she was down the river with Dr. Frank. I wandered down the path, but they were not in sight. I waited for about eight minutes and walked back. All the natives except the house boy had gone to sleep in their huts. I did not see the house boy for some time, and when I did I was frightened by the fear on his face.

I was coming round by the old ox-stalls, now deserted — since Sonia had abandoned farming, even with a tractor, far less a span of oxen. The house boy appeared then, and whispered to me. 'Baas Van der Merwe is come. He looking in the window.'

I walked quietly round the stalls till I had a view of the house, and saw a man of about fifty, under-nourished-looking, in khaki shorts and shirt. He was standing on a box by the drawing-room window. He had his hand on the curtain, parting it, and was looking steadily into the empty room.

'Go down to the river and warn them,' I said to the boy.

He turned to go, but 'Boy!' shouted the man. The house boy in his green-and-white clothes rapidly went towards the voice.

I got down to the river just as they were landing. Sonia was dressed in pale blue. Her new parasol was blue. She looked specially fabulous and I noticed her very white teeth, her round brown eyes and her story-book pose, as she stood dressed up in the middle of Africa under the blazing sun with the thick-leaved plants at her feet. Frank, looking nice in tropical suiting, was tying up the punt. 'Your husband has returned,' I said, and ran fearfully back to my car. I started it up and made off, and as I sped past the house over the gravel I saw Jannie Van der Merwe about to enter the house, followed by the servant. He turned to watch my car and spoke to the native, evidently asking who I was.

Afterwards the native deposed that Jannie went all through the house examining the changes and the new furniture. He used the lavatory and pulled the chain. He tried the taps in both bathrooms. In Sonia's room he put straight a pair of her shoes which were lying askew. He then tested all the furniture for dust, all through the house, touching the furniture with the middle finger of his right hand and turning up his finger to see if it showed any dust. The house boy followed, and when Jannie came to an old oak Dutch chest which was set away in a corner of one of the children's rooms — since Sonia had taken against all her father's old furniture — he found a little dust on it. He ordered the native to fetch a duster and remove the dust. When this was done Jannie proceeded on his tour, and when he had tried everything for dust he went out and down the path towards the river. He found Sonia and Frank at the ox-stalls arguing about what to do and where to go, and taking a revolver from his pocket, shot them. Sonia died immediately. Frank lingered for ten hours. This was a serious crime and Jannie was hanged.

I waited all the weeks ahead for Richard to make the first suggestion that we should move away. I was afraid to suggest it first lest he should resent the move all his life. Our long leave was not due for another year. Our annual leave was not due for some months. At last he said, 'I can't stand it here.'

85

I wanted to return to England. I had been thinking of nothing else.

'We can't stay here,' I said, as if it were a part in a play.

'Shall we pack up and go?' he said, and I felt a huge relief.

'No,' I said.

He said, 'It would be a pity to pack it all in when we've both gone so far in tropical diseases.'

In fact I left the following week. Since then, Richard has gone far in tropical diseases. 'It's a pity,' he said before I left, 'to let what's happened come between us.'

I packed up my things and departed for dear life, before the dry season should set in, and the rainy season should follow, and all things be predictable.

The Dry River Bed

CAST

Marjorie	The Nurse
Borden	Grace
Ticky	Lucia
Sarah	Martha

(*Tea-party noises*)

Sarah. She was at school with Marjorie in England. Marjorie knew her well. She was to be one of Marjorie's bridesmaids.

Lucia. *Knew* her well. . . . You know, Sarah, she may still be alive. It's only a week ago that . . .

Martha. Hardly likely. No, they've killed her.

Sarah. Well, Martha, I've been twenty-five years in the Colony and we've never had a bit of trouble with our natives round here. I simply can't believe . . .

Martha. Times are changing, Sarah.

Lucia. We know nothing, really. Poor Peggy Whitehead.

Martha. We do know that she disappeared, so what do you mean that we know nothing really? The natives these days . . .

Sarah. More tea, Lucia? Martha?

Lucia. ⎫ Thanks.
Martha. ⎭ Yes, thanks.

Martha. We do know that she disappeared off the road within ten minutes and hasn't been seen since.

Lucia. Were there any fingerprints on the horse?

Martha. *Can* you have fingerprints on a horse?

Lucia. Oh, I should think so. Well, the police would know, wouldn't they? That new young trooper, Ticky Talbot, says they've explored the possibility that it may have been a leopard.

Sarah. Nonsense. A leopard would have got the horse and left the girl. These new young policemen from England and the Cape are so silly. When you've been twenty-five years in the Colony you don't talk about a leopard seizing a girl off a horse.

(*Horse's hoofbeats*)

Who's this? Look and see who it is, Martha.

Martha. It's Ticky Talbot.

Sarah. (*Calling out of the door.*) Oh, Ticky — come on in. We're on the side stoep.

(*Ticky dismounts and walks over gravel*)

Is one of the boys taking his horse?

Martha. Yes, I think so. I wonder if he's got any news of poor . . . Oh, hallo, Ticky.

Lucia. Any news of poor Peggy?

(*Business with tea cups*)

Sarah. How do you like your tea, Ticky?

Ticky. Fairly strong, please. Thanks. God, it's hot.

Sarah. You wait till you've been twenty-five years in the Colony. Lucia — fish those ants out of the sugar, will you? They get into everything; sometimes I become so furious with them. And it doesn't get you anywhere to be furious with ants, they only stream on and on.

Martha. Any news of the missing girl, Ticky?

Ticky. No, nothing new. I say, it *is* hot.

Sarah. We shall soon have the rains. It always gets like this before the rains. You haven't been here through a rainy season, have you, Ticky?

Ticky. No. None of us down at the station have, in fact.

Sarah. Sugar?

Ticky. Thanks.

Sarah. Mind you don't take an ant. Fish it out.

Ticky. The ants have got into our stores down at the station.

Martha. They've got into everyone's stores. If the natives don't pinch your stuff, the ants get it.

Lucia. Wait till the rains start, then you'll see the flying ants coming out of cracks in the walls. They wriggle out then fly all over the place. Newcomers don't like them. But you'll get used to it all.

Sarah. Now don't put Ticky off the Colony. Ticky — you'll find everything wonderful after the rains. The whole veldt is covered with cosmos, flowers that spring up overnight, all colours. Everything smells damp and . . .

Martha. And the rivers are impassable.

Ticky. I saw a dust devil today.

Lucia. Oh, that's an evil omen, to be sure.

Sarah. Take no notice of her, Ticky, she's teasing you. New people often get a fright with a dust devil. Did you get a fright?

Ticky. Well, I wondered what it was, a great column of dust dancing along the road in front of my horse. I thought the horse was going to shy, but it didn't.

Sarah. Oh, the horses are used to it. So will you be, when you've spent twenty-five years in the Colony. Borden Reeves — that's my daughter Marjorie's fiancé — has been here three years and he's only just getting used to it. You know Borden, of course, don't you, Ticky? He comes from the Cape.

Ticky. Yes. In fact I thought he might be here. Have you seen him lately?

Sarah. Well, I haven't *seen* him. But he came over here this afternoon to take Marjorie for her driving lesson. Didn't you pass them on the road?

Ticky. I passed Marjorie on the road. She was driving alone. As a matter of fact, I wondered about that. I don't like to be officious, but we all know she hasn't got her licence yet, and . . .

Sarah. Nonsense, Marjorie *can't* drive. Borden must have been sitting beside her. He's teaching Marjorie to drive so that she can take turns at the wheel when they go on their honeymoon. If you wait a little while, Ticky, they'll be back for drinks.

Ticky. Marjorie was driving alone. I'm quite sure of it.

Sarah. But she can't drive. She's only had one lesson and she didn't get on very well with that. She gets mixed up between her left and her right, that's Marjorie's trouble. Now, Ticky, you're just imagining things, it's the heat and the glare. New people are half blind from the glare. You'll get used to it.

Lucia. (*Mimicking Sarah.*) When you've been twenty-five years in the Colony . . .

Ticky. Marjorie was driving alone in your husband's Ford. She . . .

Sarah. Look, Ticky . . .

Ticky. Where has Borden left *his* car?

Sarah. Outside in the drive, I daresay. Look, out there. My eyesight's not too good, but you'll see . . .

Ticky. Borden's car isn't there.

Sarah. It must be there. Ticky, the glare of the sun's affecting . . .

Martha. No, Borden's car isn't there.

Sarah. Oh well, he must have walked over. I can't think why he would, in all this heat. Perhaps he got a lift. I suppose . . .

Ticky. Marjorie was driving alone. Down towards the river. I'm quite sure of it, because I've been trying to get hold of Borden. I've been wanting to speak to him. He hasn't been seen at the farm for three days. . . .

Sarah. Cake, Martha, Lucia. Ticky, have a piece of cake. Watch out for the ants. Look, Ticky, this is the heat. I mean to say, Borden hasn't been *away* from the farm for three days. They've had this tobacco crisis going on. Now, Ticky, I tell you he came over here an hour ago to take Marjorie for her driving lesson. He *must* have been in the car with her. If you wait for a sundowner they'll both be back and you shall see I'm right. It's too bad of you accusing poor Marjorie. . . .

Lucia. Sarah, is Borden very upset about Peggy's disappearance?

Sarah. Well, yes, we're all very upset about Peggy. If only we knew one way or the other. You know, Ticky, you police ought to look lively. I mean to say, a girl can't just disappear off a horse into the bush without leaving some trace. Apparently she was wearing that bright-blue blouse, the colour didn't suit her at all. Now can't you look for the bright-blue blouse? I mean to say, Ticky, organize a search. . . .

Ticky. We were wondering if Borden might have some suggestions. He seemed to know Peggy rather well.

Martha. Borden?

Sarah. Borden has been busy with his tobacco. And when he's not busy with his tobacco he's busy with Marjorie. They've got their wedding plans to make. I do wish this hadn't happened. Peggy was to have been a bridesmaid.

Lucia. Her aunt refuses to believe she's dead.

Sarah. Oh, her aunt won't face the facts.

Martha. No one will face the facts. The natives aren't what they used to be. Things are changing rapidly, and . . .

(Car drives up)

Sarah. Look out and see who it is, Martha. I daresay it's Marjorie and Borden come back.

Martha. No, it's Grace.

(Bang of car door)

The Dry River Bed

Sarah. (*Calling out of doors.*) Come on in, Grace. Haven't seen *you* for a long time.

Grace. Martha — Lucia. Hallo, Mr. Talbot. I haven't been able to leave the farm for ages, what with this tobacco fuss and the labour problem. It's a dull world. I see Marjorie has learnt to drive. I passed her about twenty miles along the road, and there she was spinning along all by herself.

Ticky.⎱ By herself?
Lucia.⎰ Alone? Borden wasn't with her?

Sarah. Tea, Grace? Everyone's going mad. Marjorie doesn't know how to drive a car. She's gone out for a lesson with Borden.

Grace. No, no. She was driving by herself. My dear, is Marjorie all right? What I mean is, I waved, but she didn't seem to see me. She seemed to be talking to herself. I wondered, in fact, if I ought to turn and follow. She was racing along towards the river, much too fast — towards the river bed I mean — you can hardly call it a river when it's dry, can you? And it is rather dangerous, Sarah, to drive at speed down there. You know what those deep wagon ruts are like. They simply carry you right in, you simply lose control of a wheel. And you know what it's like if you land a car in a dry river bed.

(Fade)

(Noise to suggest a hospital, such as footsteps on bare floor
— so that scene will be recognised when repeated later)

Ticky. Nurse, I think I saw her eyelids move.

Nurse. She'll be coming round in a moment, Sergeant Talbot. Just don't rush her. She may be a bit vague to start with, a little . . .

93

Ticky. I could come back later if . . .

Marjorie. Ticky, what are you doing here? Are you real?

Nurse. You're in hospital, Marjorie; it's only a little . . .

Marjorie. Have I had an accident?

Nurse. That's right, you had a car crash yesterday. You went straight into a dry river bed, silly girl. You will probably feel a little . . .

Marjorie. Any bones broken?

Nurse. No, only a little bruise here and there. You got the wheel bang on the chest and a mysterious bump on the back, but it's only a little . . .

Marjorie. And I've had concussion.

Nurse. Yes, you're bound to feel a little . . .

Marjorie. Ticky, what are you doing here? Have I done a crime?

Ticky. Well, Marjorie, if you aren't feeling up to questions I'll come back. It's only that we want to find Borden rather quickly. I thought you might know . . .

Nurse. Do you feel able to answer Sergeant Talbot's questions, Marjorie? If not, perhaps we could wait a little while, and . . .

Marjorie. Sit down, Ticky.

Nurse. Well, I'll leave you to Sergeant Talbot.

Marjorie. Yes, just for a little while.

(*Nurse leaves*)

Ticky. It's rather urgent, Marjorie. We're looking for Borden. When did you last see him?

Marjorie. When did I crash into the dry river bed?

94

Ticky. Yesterday afternoon.

Marjorie. That's when I last saw Borden.

Ticky. Are you sure? There wasn't any trace of him in the river bed when we discovered you there.

Marjorie. Didn't you find anything else, though? Didn't you discover . . .

Ticky. Yes, you know we did. Take it quietly, Marjorie.

Marjorie. What did you find?

Ticky. The remains of Peggy Whitehead. She was half buried beneath a pile of stones. You must have got out of the car after the crash, and you must have lifted up the stones where she was buried, and you must have . . .

Marjorie. No, Borden displaced the stones.

Ticky. Marjorie, you must have . . .

Marjorie. I hadn't seen Borden for a week. You know they had that tobacco crisis and there was a meeting in the capital. Then the trouble with the farm boys. So he didn't come to see me all week. But yesterday morning he telephoned to say he'd be over after lunch to take me for my driving lesson.

Ticky. You must have . . .

Marjorie. So Borden walked over after lunch. He didn't come into the house, just waited for me in the drive. I'm quite lucid, Ticky, so listen. I thought he was rather rude, not coming in to say hallo to Mother. But you know how moody Borden was . . . is . . . was.

Ticky. Was . . .?

Marjorie. I'm not sure if Borden is still alive . . . or perhaps half alive.

Ticky. We believe he's still alive. He left the Colony a week ago but we think he's still in Africa.

Marjorie. A week ago! In that case . . . oh, in that case . . . Ticky, I'd better tell you what happened yesterday. I got into the driving seat and we set off north towards the river valley.

(Fade)

Borden. Slow down, darling, that's the *clutch* you're pressing. Right foot, Marjorie, *right* foot. That's it, now change down. God, don't you know up from down? Change down — here, let me do it. You've got to put the lever down for uphill.

Marjorie. Oh, Borden, you'd better take over. I don't think I shall ever learn to drive. *(Sound of car swerving.)* Goodness, what was that?

Borden. Only a buck jumping out of the bush across the road. You'll have to learn not to swerve for a buck. You just drive straight on and *over* a buck. That fixes him. Carry on.

Marjorie. Oh, I couldn't . . .

Borden. You've shot a buck, haven't you?

Marjorie. Yes, but running it over is different. Can't I stop now?

Borden. Turn in to the side. . . . No, not the right — the left. Don't cross the road; pull in to the *left*. No, that's too sharp, you'll land us both in the bush — let me. *(Car pulls up.)*
You really must learn to distinguish left from right and up from down.

Marjorie. (*Edgily.*) And black from white.

Borden. What do you mean? What do you mean by that, exactly?

Marjorie. Nothing, dear, I'm just having a little joke. Calm down.

Borden. What do you mean, you must learn to distinguish black from white?

Marjorie. It's just a little rhyme — left from right, up from down, black from white. I wish the rains would come and then people could be nice to each other again. I just don't see why you're making all this fuss.

Borden. Has anyone been advising you not to marry me?

Marjorie. Not lately. They've given up. But if you're going to talk to me like that and *look* at me like that, I'm damned if I'm going to marry you.

Borden. All right, all right. Sorry. I've been worried about the tobacco and I suppose the heat . . .

Marjorie. Well, let's get on with the lesson. What do I do now? Left foot on the clutch, right . . .

Borden. Ignition switch first.

Marjorie. Of course. (*Starts up car — drives off jerkily.*)

Borden. Don't crash the gears, darling. Neutral — down — forward, back then down — gently, don't *crash* them — look, let me . . .

Marjorie. You're putting me off my steering. I should have got Ticky Talbot to teach me. He offered to. How can I steer when you . . .

Borden. You've got other things to do in driving besides steer. You can't just steer. What are you accelerating for? . . . Look out, there's another car coming. Go on to the left-hand strip and let him have a bit of tarmac. No need to go *all* off the tarmac, dear — just take the left strip and let him pass. Don't *accelerate*. Footbrake in the middle. Take your *right* foot off the accelerator.

(*Other car passes*)

Marjorie, you'll have to learn to slow down when a car passes. Now here's a chap on a horse coming over the hill, so go slow. It's a police chap, and he'll probably be giving you your driving test, so go slow.

Marjorie. Oh, it's Ticky Talbot.

Borden. Slow. Don't press the accelerator. Take your *right* foot off. . . .

(*Car whizzes past horse*)

Your *right* foot . . . that's it. Now into the side of the road and pull up.

Marjorie. I did try to go slow, but I couldn't.

(*Their car pulling up*)

Borden. Have you ever had trouble in distinguishing left from right before? I mean, if it's something constitutional we'd better give up.

Marjorie. No, I want to learn to drive. It's only that you . . .

Borden. Well, I'm sure you didn't impress Ticky just now.

Marjorie. I wasn't thinking of impressing Ticky. Do you know what I was thinking? I was thinking I can't possibly marry you.

Borden. It's the heat, it's the driving lesson . . . you're getting nervy.

Marjorie. You used to go riding with Peggy Whitehead, didn't you?

Borden. My dear, that was a year ago.

Marjorie. When Peggy was at school with me in England she could never keep on a horse. But you taught her to ride. And now look what's happened to Peggy.

Borden. We don't know what's happened to Peggy. Do we?

Marjorie. How should I know if we do or if we don't. All I know is . . .

Borden. What the hell are you suggesting . . .

Marjorie. I'm not suggesting anything. Perhaps I'm superstitious. Perhaps you were unlucky to Peggy. If she hadn't known how to ride she would never . . . Oh, I can't think straight. I can't drive. I can't tell left from right, up from down, black from white . . .

Borden. What are you saying?

Marjorie. Let's continue with the lesson. I'm determined to do this. Ignition switch. Clutch, lever in neutral, forward-up, forward-back.

(*Car starts up — fade*)
(*Hospital noise*)

Ticky. Look, are you comfortable?

Marjorie. Just move this pillow a bit. . . .

Ticky. Don't talk any more. You mustn't become excited. Look, I'd better get a nurse. . . .

Marjorie. No, I must tell you, Ticky. It was the last lap of the driving lesson . . . I . . .

(*Nurse comes in*)

Nurse. Take this little tablet, Marjorie. Sip this little glass of . . .

Marjorie. (*Gulping water.*) Will it send me to sleep? I do want to talk to Ticky. I haven't got sunstroke now, I'm perfectly . . .

Nurse. The pill should calm you down a bit, it won't send you to sleep. Now you can talk to the Sergeant for a while. . . . But don't overdo it. Your mother's coming to see you a little later.

(*Nurse goes out*)

Marjorie. Sit down, Ticky. Don't keep standing up and sitting down again. Ticky, after you passed us on your horse Borden and I had this quarrel. I started up the car again — I was determined to master it — and drove it. I may have had a touch of the sun — I don't know. Ticky, I drove beautifully, but terribly fast. I felt as if Borden was driving *me*. I even told him to slow down, but of course that was silly because I was at the wheel. We were approaching the river. I knew we would soon be in danger of those great wagon ruts where the oxen go down to drink. Do you know the great ruts, Ticky? Always be careful to avoid them in the dry season. Once you drive your car into them you can't get out, they carry you straight down to the river bed.

Ticky. It was only a touch of sunstroke, Marjorie. I'm sure you'll make a good driver when you learn properly.

Marjorie. I remember passing Grace Chalmers in her car. She was on the way to Mother's tea-party, I suppose. We were approaching the river. I went on and on. . . .

(Fade)   *(Car)*

(Rapidly.) That was Grace Chalmers on her way to Mother's tea-party, I suppose. I expect they're all going to discuss the disappearance of Peggy Whitehead. Poor Peggy, I expect someone will come across her body one day. At least, what's left of her body, with all these ants — nothing but a few bones dressed up in Peggy's breeches and bright-blue blouse. I can't believe the natives would . . .

Borden. Carry on, straight on, down to the bridge. You're doing splendidly.

Marjorie. We're going too fast. Can't we stop? Slow down, Borden, do slow down. I mean, *I* must slow down. Tell me what to do . . .

Borden. You're doing very well. Keep on. Go faster.

Marjorie. But the great wagon ruts. I'm afraid of those dry cart ruts. We might go into the river bed.

Borden. Faster, Marjorie.

Marjorie. Stop, Borden. How do I stop? How do I tell black from white — no, left from . . .

Borden. You've been told, haven't you, that I'm half black? Peggy Whitehead told you before she disappeared.

Marjorie. No, she didn't tell me you were half black, Borden.

Borden. Look at me.

Marjorie. I have looked at you, many times.

Borden. Look at me.

Marjorie. I can't. I've got to keep my eyes on the road. That's what you're always telling me. 'Keep your eyes on the road', you say; isn't that what you say? Oh, I want to stop.

Borden. Go on, go faster. Look at me. (*Car speeds up.*) Look.

Marjorie. How white you've gone! Are you afraid of something?

Borden. Notice my broad nostrils. See my lips. A touch of the negroid, wouldn't you say?

Marjorie. You've gone frightfully pale, Borden. What's happened?

Borden. You've gone down to sixty-five. You can do seventy, eighty. We're coming to the river. See the bridge ahead. . . .

Marjorie. Borden, look, we're going away from the bridge. Take the wheel quickly. Pull the brake. We're in a huge rut. I can't move the wheel.

Borden. Carry on. You're doing fine.

Marjorie. The brake, Borden. Take the wheel. We're going into the river bed. We'll crash. I . . .

Borden. Carry straight on.

(*Crash. Fade out and in*)

(*Hospital*)

Ticky. Carry on. . . .

Marjorie. The heat was terrific. I didn't have a hat. I don't know how I got out of the car. I didn't see Borden at first. Then I saw him standing about fifty yards away, waiting for me.

Ticky. Waiting?

Marjorie. Yes, that's what he was doing. He didn't make any move to help me or see if I was all right. He was just waiting for me to get out of the car. There was broken glass everywhere. Borden just stood waiting beside a mound of stones. Of course, I was dazed. The thing that struck me as most odd just then was the mound of stones. You know those burial piles — you must have seen, here and there on the veldt, those piles of loose stones.

Ticky. Yes, they've been pointed out to me.

Marjorie. That's how the natives bury their dead. They place them in a sitting-up position and just pile the stones around the corpse. Well, Borden was standing by a pile of stones like that. I thought, how odd to see a burial place in a dry river bed. The natives would never bury their dead there. (*Garbled speech.*) You see, I'm just telling you, Ticky, what passed through my mind when I got out of the wreck.

Ticky. Speak a bit more slowly, Marjorie. Don't try too hard. Just talk. What were you saying?

Marjorie. I'm just telling you, Ticky, what passed through my mind when I got out of the wreck of the car. Don't speak to me as if you were a psychiatrist. I'm perfectly lucid in my mind.

Ticky. Are you sure?

Marjorie. Yes.

Ticky. Then it's really most interesting.

Marjorie. Borden spoke first. He said, 'My head has been injured on the windscreen. My head's been cut open.'

Ticky. Was his head cut?

Marjorie. Yes, but there was no blood. I saw long deep cuts all over his face, but they were white and dry. I turned round and looked at the car with the front smashed in. As I turned, something hit me in the back. It was a stone. Borden was picking up stones from the pile, one after another, and throwing them at me. You know there wasn't any way out of the river bed. I ran and took shelter behind the wreck of the car. Borden didn't follow me, but kept on lifting stones from the burial pile and throwing them at the car, as if I'd been still there in sight, instead of crouching behind the car. The sun was beating down on the dry river bed. Nothing is quite so dry as a dry river bed, not even the desert. Because it's a place where water should be. I called out, 'Borden, why are your scars so white and dry? Why is there nothing where your blood should be?'

(*Sound of stones thudding on car throughout the following*)
(*Voices speaking at distance of 50 yards*)

Borden. Because I'm only half here. Flesh without blood.

Marjorie. Borden, where is your blood?

Borden. Waiting for me at Mombasa, fifteen hundred miles away.

Marjorie. Borden, why are you throwing those stones at me?

Borden. Because I want to get rid of the stones.

Marjorie. What have you got under the stones, Borden?

Borden. A bright-blue blouse, riding breeches, riding boots, girl's underwear, bones, a large formation of ants.

Marjorie. Borden, why did you kill her?

Borden. She intended to stop our marriage. She intended to tell you I was half-caste. Half black, half white.

Marjorie. I knew it, Borden. I've always known. Why are you throwing stones at me?

Borden. I should like to kill you.

Marjorie. You can't. You're only half here.

Borden. I can take half your life.

Marjorie. You've done that already.

Borden. Goodbye, then. (*Whirlwind sound.*)

Marjorie. Borden, where are you going?

Borden. (*Receding.*) To Mombasa to join my black blood. Who is waiting for me now, down at the harbour.

Marjorie. Why are you spinning round and round like a dust devil?

Borden. Do you know what causes a whirlwind?— *Dryness.*

Marjorie. You can't go up a dry river bed in all this heat. Borden, come back. Give yourself up to the police. Go and see Ticky Talbot . . . Give yourself up to Ticky . . .

(*Tea-party noises*)

Sarah. She was at school with Marjorie in England. As I say, Marjorie knew her well. She was to be one of Marjorie's bridesmaids. . . .

Lucia. Sarah, don't upset yourself. I never did take to Borden. Most unsuitable for Marjorie. None of us thought him any good for Marjorie.

Sarah. Marjorie wanted to get up to go to Peggy's funeral. Of course, it was out of the question.

Martha. There must have been very little left to bury. The ants . . .

Lucia. Martha!

Martha. Is Marjorie's . . . brain a little better now, Sarah?

Sarah. She realises she had a bad attack of sunstroke the day she drove off alone like that. Tea, Lucia?

Lucia. How did she manage to *drive* the car, that's what I'd like to know.

Sarah. Tea, Martha? She didn't manage to drive it very well, did she?

Martha. How did she find the exact place where Peggy was buried, that's what I'd like to know.

Sarah. More tea, Martha?

Lucia. Yes, and how did she manage to move those stones when she'd just been injured in a car crash?

Sarah. Cake, Lucia?

Lucia. And this story of hers — there's no use blinding yourself to it, Sarah. We hear news from the hospital — Marjorie's been saying such silly things. She says Borden's half white and half black, which we all suspected, to tell the truth. But she says his white half was with her on the afternoon of the crash and his black half was in Mombasa. Can't you get her to see a specialist, or something . . . ?

Sarah. Cake, Martha? Fish those ants out of the sugar, will you?

Martha. What puzzles me . . .

Lucia.   It isn't my business, I know, but . . .

(*Sound of horse*)

Sarah. Martha, glance out and see who it is.

Martha. It's Ticky Talbot. I wonder where *he's* been the last few days. He hasn't . . .

Sarah. (*Calling.*) Ticky, we're out on the stoep. Come along. Where have you been the last few days?

Ticky. I've been in Mombasa. I just got back this morning.

Martha. Mombasa. . . . Surely you aren't due for leave yet, Ticky?

Lucia. Some people are awfully lucky.

Sarah. Tea, Ticky. Fairly weak and . . .

Ticky. No, fairly strong. Thanks.

Martha. Well, where *have* you been?

Ticky. I went on police duties. We were after Borden.

Lucia. You didn't take any notice of that story of Marjorie's? Ticky, the sun must be affecting you all down at the station. Borden is probably in South America or somewhere by now. He gave you the slip properly.

Ticky. We got Borden at Mombasa.

Sarah. }
Martha. } You got Borden!

Martha. He must have confided the whole thing to Marjorie. She may have been an accomplice. Of course, Sarah, I mean an *innocent* accomplice . . .

Sarah. Sugar, Ticky. Mind the ants.

Ticky. We were watching Mombasa for Borden as soon as he disappeared, in fact. On the afternoon of the car crash a fellow cashed a cheque in the name of Borden Reeves.

Lucia. *Was* it Borden?

Ticky. He was a black fellow. He was traced to a native café on the harbour. We questioned him, but we couldn't get anything out of him except that his name was, curiously enough, Borden Reeves. We searched the café but there was no sign of Borden. We kept watch on the café after that.

Martha. The native must have been in league with Borden.

Ticky. Obviously, in a way. Yesterday, a man resembling Borden arrived in Mombasa by plane.

Lucia. Was it Borden?

Ticky. Not exactly. We couldn't prove it. I was brought along to identify him, but the chap certainly wasn't Borden exactly. He was terribly pale and anaemic looking. We let him go, eventually, but we had him followed. He went straight to the café by the harbour and went upstairs. A few hours later Borden himself came out of the café.

Lucia. Was he really Borden?

Ticky. Yes.

Lucia. He must have been hiding there all this time.

Ticky. No, we were quite sure he hadn't been hiding in the café.

Sarah. So you've got Borden?

Ticky. We arrested him on a charge of murder. He took out a gun and shot himself. I've never seen so much blood in all my life.

Lucia. Really, you troopers are quite mad. You're as bad as Marjorie. . . .

Martha. I should think there would be an enquiry into all this. We settlers are absolutely dependent on the police. If we can't depend on them in the dry season . . .

Ticky. Well, we did get Borden.

Martha. What about the black fellow and the pale one?

Ticky. So far as we're concerned, they don't exist. We had no charge against them.

Sarah. Does Marjorie know what has happened?

Ticky. Yes. In fact I went straight to the hospital to tell her. She seemed to come alive. I'm sure she will be better now. She said she'd been feeling half in the world and half out of it . . .

Lucia. Ticky, I think you boys should keep out of the sun, really . . .

Sarah. Well, Lucia, when you've been twenty-five years in the Colony you realise the sort of things that happen at the end of the dry season. We'll have the rains soon.

(*Whirring sound*)

Who's that? Martha, look out and see who it is, will you?

Martha. I can't quite see. One of the native boys coming home drunk, I should say . . . He's doing a dance. . . .

Sarah. Nonsense, Martha. Who *is* it?

Lucia. (*Laughs.*)

Sarah. Let *me* see. Who on earth . . . Oh . . . it's only a dust devil. Look there, Ticky. . . .

Ticky. Yes, I *have seen* one.

The Dark Glasses

COMING to the edge of the lake we paused to look at our reflections in the water. It was then I recognised her from the past, her face looking up from the lake. She had not stopped talking.

I put on my dark glasses to shield my eyes from the sun and conceal my recognition from her eyes.

'Am I boring you?' she said.

'No, not a bit, Dr. Gray.'

'Sure?'

It is discouraging to put on sun glasses in the middle of someone's intimate story. But they were necessary, now that I had recognised her, and was excited, and could only honourably hear what she had to say from a point of concealment.

'Must you wear those glasses?'

'Well, yes. The glare.'

'The wearing of dark glasses,' she said, 'is a modern psychological phenomenon. It signifies the trend towards impersonalisation, the weapon of the modern Inquisitor, it——'

'There's a lot in what you say.' But I did not remove my glasses, for I had not asked for her company in the first place, and there is a limit to what one can listen to with the naked eye.

We walked round the new concrete verge of the old lake, and she continued the story of how she was led to give up general medical practice and take up psychology; and I looked at her as she spoke through my dark glasses, and because of the softening effect these have upon things I saw her again as I had seen her looking up from the lake, and again as in my childhood.

At the end of the 'thirties Leesden End was an L-shaped town. Our house stood near the top of the L. At the other extreme was the market. Mr. Simmonds, the oculist, had his shop on the horizontal leg, and he lived there above the shop with his mother and sister. All the other shops in the row were attached to each other, but Mr. Simmonds' stood apart, like a real house, with a lane on either side.

I was sent to have my eyes tested. He took me into the darkened interior and said, 'Sit down, dear.' He put his arm round my shoulder. His forefinger moved up and down on my neck. I was thirteen and didn't like to be rude to him. Dorothy Simmonds, his sister, came downstairs just then; she came upon us silently and dressed in a white overall. Before she had crossed the room to switch on a dim light Mr. Simmonds removed his arm from my shoulder with such a jerk that I knew for certain he had not placed it there in innocence.

I had seen Miss Simmonds once before, at a garden fête, where she stood on a platform in a big hat and blue dress, and sang 'Sometimes between long shadows on the grass', while I picked up windfall apples, all of which seemed to be rotten. Now in her white overall she turned and gave me a hostile look, as if I had been seducing her brother. I felt sexually in the wrong, and started looking round the dark room with a wide-eyed air.

'Can you read?' said Mr. Simmonds.

I stopped looking round. I said, 'Read what?' — for I had been told I would be asked to read row after row of letters. The card which hung beneath the dim light showed pictures of trains and animals.

'Because if you can't read we have pictures for illiterates.'

This was Mr. Simmonds' joke. I giggled. His sister smiled and dabbed her right eye with her handkerchief. She had been to London for an operation on her right eye.

I recall reading the letters correctly down to the last few lines, which were too small. I recall Mr. Simmonds squeezing my arm as I left the shop, turning his sandy freckled face in a backward glance to see for certain that his sister was not watching.

My grandmother said, 'Did you see——'

'— Mr. Simmonds' sister?' said my aunt.

'Yes, she was there all the time,' I said, to make it definite.

My grandmother said, 'They say she's going——'

'— blind in one eye,' said my aunt.

'And with the mother bedridden upstairs——' my grandmother said.

'— she must be a saint,' said my aunt.

Presently — it may have been within a few days or a few weeks — my reading glasses arrived, and I wore them whenever I remembered to do so.

I broke the glasses by sitting on them during my school holidays two years later.

My grandmother said, after she had sighed, 'It's time you had your eyes tested——'

'— eyes tested in any case,' said my aunt when she had sighed.

I washed my hair the night before and put a wave in it. Next morning at eleven I walked down to Mr. Simmonds' with one of my grandmother's long hatpins in my blazer pocket. The shop front had been done up, with gold lettering on the glass door: Basil Simmonds, Optician, followed by a string of letters which, so far as I remember, were F.B.O.A., A.I.C., and others.

'You're quite the young lady, Joan,' he said, looking at my new breasts.

I smiled and put my hand in my blazer pocket.

He was smaller than he had been two years ago. I thought he must be about fifty or thirty. His face was more freckled than ever and his eyes were flat blue as from a box of paints. Miss Simmonds appeared silently in her soft slippers. 'You're quite the young lady, Joan,' she said from behind her green glasses, for her right eye had now gone blind and the other was said to be troubling her.

We went into the examination room. She glided past me and switched on the dim light above the letter card. I began to read out the letters while Basil Simmonds stood with folded hands. Someone came into the front shop. Miss Simmonds slid off to see who it was and her brother tickled my neck. I read on. He drew me towards him. I put my hand into my blazer pocket. He said, 'Oh!' and sprang away as the hat-pin struck through my blazer and into his thigh.

Miss Simmonds appeared in the doorway in her

113

avenging white overall. Her brother, who had been rubbing his thigh in a puzzled way, pretended to be dusting a mark off the front of his trousers.

'What's wrong? Why did you shout?' she said.

'No, I didn't shout.'

She looked at me, then returned to attend to the person in the shop, leaving the intervening door wide open. She was back again almost immediately. My examination was soon over. Mr. Simmonds saw me out at the front door and gave me a pleading unhappy look. I felt like a traitor and I considered him horrible.

For the rest of the holidays I thought of him as 'Basil', and by asking questions and taking more interest than usual in the conversation around me I formed an idea of his private life. 'Dorothy,' I speculated, 'and Basil.' I let my mind dwell on them until I saw a picture of the rooms above the shop. I hung round at tea-time and, in order to bring the conversation round to Dorothy and Basil, told our visitors I had been to get my eyes tested.

'The mother bedridden all these years and worth a fortune. But what good is it to her?'

'What chance is there for Miss Simmonds now, with that eye?'

'She'll get the money. He will get the bare legal minimum only.'

'No, they say he's to get everything. In trust.'

'I believe Mrs. Simmonds has left everything to her daughter.'

My grandmother said, 'She should divide her fortune——'

'—— equally between them,' said my aunt. 'Fair's fair.'

I invented for myself a recurrent scene in which brother and sister emerged from their mother's room and, on the narrow landing, allowed their gaze to meet in unspoken combat over their inheritance. Basil's flat-coloured eyes did not themselves hold any expression, but by the forward thrust of his red neck he indicated his meaning; Dorothy made herself plain by means of a corkscrew twist of the head — round and up — and the glitter of her one good eye through the green glasses.

I was sent for to try on my new reading glasses. I had the hat-pin with me. I was friendly to Basil while I tested the new glasses in the front shop. He seemed to want to put a hand on my shoulder, hovered, but was afraid. Dorothy came downstairs and appeared before us just as his hand wavered. He protracted the wavering gesture into one which adjusted the stem of my glasses above my ear.

'Auntie says to try them properly,' I said, 'while I'm about it.' This gave me an opportunity to have a look round the front premises.

'You'll only want them for your studies,' Basil said.

'Oh, I sometimes need glasses even when I'm not reading,' I said. I was looking through a door into a small inner office, darkened by a tree outside in the lane. The office contained a dumpy green safe, an old typewriter on a table, and a desk in the window with a ledger on it. Other ledgers were placed——

'Nonsense,' Dorothy was saying. 'A healthy girl like you — you hardly need glasses at all. For reading, to save your eyes, perhaps *yes*. But when you're not reading . . .'

I said, 'Grandmother said to enquire after your mother.'

'She's failing,' she said.

I took to giving Basil a charming smile when I passed him in the street on the way to the shops. This was very frequently. And on these occasions he would be standing at his shop door awaiting my return; then I would snub him. I wondered how often he was prepared to be won and rejected within the same ten minutes.

I took walks before supper round the back lanes, ambling right round the Simmonds' house, thinking of what was going on inside. One dusky time it started to rain heavily, and I found I could reasonably take shelter under the tree which grew quite close to the grimy window of the inner office. I could just see over the ledge and make out a shape of a person sitting at the desk. Soon, I thought, the shape will have to put on the light.

After five minutes' long waiting time the shape arose and switched on the light by the door. It was Basil, suddenly looking pink-haired. As he returned to the desk he stooped and took from the safe a sheaf of papers held in the teeth of a large clip. I knew he was going to select one sheet of paper from the sheaf, and that this one document would be the exciting, important one. It was like reading a familiar book: one knew what was coming, but couldn't bear to miss a word. He did extract one long sheet of paper, and hold it up. It was typewritten with a paragraph in handwriting at the bottom on the side visible from the window. He laid it side by side with another sheet of paper which was lying on the desk. I pressed close up to the window, intending to wave and smile if I was seen, and to call out that I was sheltering from the rain which was now coming down in thumps. But he kept his eyes on the two sheets of paper. There were other papers lying about the desk; I could not see what was on them. But I was quite convinced that he had been practising hand-writing on them, and that he was in the process of forging his mother's will.

Then he took up the pen. I can still smell the rain and hear it thundering about me, and feel it dripping on my head from the bough overhanging above me. He raised his eyes and looked out at the rain. It seemed his eyes rested on me, at my station between the tree and the window. I kept still and close to the tree like a hunted piece of nature, willing myself to be the colour of bark and leaves and rain. Then I realised how much more clearly I could see him than he me, for it was growing dark.

He pulled a sheet of blotting paper towards him. He dipped his pen in the ink and started writing on the bottom of the sheet of paper before him, comparing it from time to time with the one he had taken out of the safe. I was not surprised, but I was thrilled, when the door behind him slowly opened. It was like seeing the film of the book. Dorothy advanced on her creeping feet, and he did not hear, but formed the words he was writing, on and on. The rain pelted down regard-less. She was looking crookedly, through her green glasses with her one eye, over his shoulder at the paper.

'What are you doing?' she said.

He jumped up and pulled the blotting paper over his work. Her one eye through her green glasses glinted upon him, though I did not actually see it do so, but saw only the dark green glass focused with a squint on to his face.

'I'm making up the accounts,' he said, standing with his back to the desk, concealing the papers. I saw his hand reach back and tremble among them.

I shivered in my soaking wet clothes. Dorothy looked with her eye at the window. I slid sideways to avoid her and ran all the way home.

Next morning I said, 'I've tried to read with these glasses. It's all a blur. I suppose I'll *have* to take them back?'

'Didn't you notice anything wrong when you tried——'

'— tried them on in the shop?'

'No. But the shop's so dark. *Must* I take them back?'

I took them into Mr. Simmonds early that afternoon.

'I tried to read with them this morning, but it's all a blur.' It was true that I had smeared them with cold cream first.

Dorothy was beside us in no time. She peered one-eyed at the glasses, then at me.

'Are you constipated?' she said.

I maintained silence. But I felt she was seeing everything through her green glasses.

'Put them on,' Dorothy said.

'Try them on,' said Basil.

They were ganged up together. Everything was going wrong, for I had come here to see how matters stood between them after the affair of the will.

Basil gave me something to read. 'It's all right now,' I said, 'but it was all a blur when I tried to read this morning.'

'Better take a dose,' Dorothy said.

I wanted to get out of the shop with my glasses as quickly as possible, but the brother said, 'I'd better test your eyes again while you're here just to make sure.'

He seemed quite normal. I followed him into the dark interior. Dorothy switched on the light. They both seemed normal. The scene in the little office last night began to lose its conviction. As I read out the letters on the card in front of me I was thinking of Basil as 'Mr. Simmonds' and Dorothy as 'Miss Simmonds', and feared their authority, and was in the wrong.

'That seems to be all right,' Mr. Simmonds said. 'But wait a moment.' He produced some coloured slides with lettering on them.

Miss Simmonds gave me what appeared to be a triumphant one-eyed leer, and as one who washes her hands of a person, started to climb the stairs. Plainly, she knew I had lost my attraction for her brother.

But before she turned the bend in the stairs she stopped and came down again. She went to a row of shelves and shifted some bottles. I read on. She interrupted:

'My eye-drops, Basil. I made them up this morning. Where are they?'

Mr. Simmonds was suddenly watching her as if something inconceivable was happening.

'Wait, Dorothy. Wait till I've tested the girl's eyes.'

She had lifted down a small brown bottle. 'I want my eye-drops. I wish you wouldn't displace—— Are these they?'

I noted her correct phrase, 'Are these they?' and it seemed just over the border of correctness. Perhaps, after all, this brother and sister were strange, vicious, in the wrong.

She had raised the bottle and was reading the label with her one good eye. 'Yes, this is mine. It has my name on it,' she said.

Dark Basil, dark Dorothy. There was something wrong after all. She walked upstairs with her bottle of eye-drops. The brother put his hand on my elbow and heaved me to my feet, forgetting his coloured slides.

'There's nothing wrong with your eyes. Off you go.' He pushed me into the front shop. His flat eyes were wide open as he handed me my glasses. He pointed to the door. 'I'm a busy man,' he said.

From upstairs came a long scream. Basil jerked open the door for me, but I did not move. Then Dorothy, upstairs, screamed and screamed and screamed. Basil put his hands to his head, covering his eyes. Dorothy appeared on the bend of the stairs, screaming, doubled-up, with both hands covering her good eye.

I started screaming when I got home, and was given a sedative. By evening everyone knew that Miss Simmonds had put the wrong drops in her eyes.

'Will she go blind in that eye, too?' people said.

'The doctor says there's hope.'

'There will be an enquiry.'

'She was going blind in that eye in any case,' they said.

'Ah, but the pain . . .'

'Who's mistake, hers or his?'

'Joan was there at the time. Joan heard the screams. We had to give her a sedative to calm——'

had a glass half-filled with sherry. Dr. Gray swung her legs, she was in the wrong, sexy, like our morning help who sat on the kitchen table swinging her legs.

But then she spoke. 'It will take time,' she said. 'A very difficult patient, of course.'

Basil nodded. Dr. Gray swung her legs, and looked professional. She was in the right, she looked like our games mistress who sometimes sat on a desk swinging her legs.

Before I returned to school I saw Basil one morning at his shop door. 'Reading glasses all right now?' he said.

'Oh yes, thank you.'

'There's nothing wrong with your sight. Don't let your imagination run away with you.'

I walked on, certain that he had known my guilty suspicions all along.

'I took up psychology during the war. Up till then I was in general practice.'

I had come to the summer school to lecture on history and she on psychology. Psychiatrists are very often ready to talk to strangers about their inmost lives. This is probably because they spend so much time hearing out their patients. I did not recognise Dr. Gray, except as a type, when I had attended her first lecture on 'the psychic manifestations of sex'. She spoke of child-poltergeists, and I was bored, and took refuge in observing the curious language of her profession. I noticed the word 'arousement'. 'Adolescents in a state of sexual arousement,' she said, 'may become possessed of almost psychic insight.'

After lunch, since the Eng. Lit. people had gone off

to play tennis, she tacked on to me and we walked to the lake across the lawns, past the rhododendrons. This lake had once been the scene of a love-mad duchess's death.

'. . . during the war. Before that I was in general practice. It's strange,' she said, 'how I came to take up psychology. My second husband had a breakdown and was under a psychiatrist. Of course, he's incurable, but I decided . . . It's strange, but that's how I came to take it up. It saved *my* reason. My husband is still in a home. His sister, of course, became quite incurable. *He* has his lucid moments. I did not realise it, of course, when I married, but there was what I'd now call an oedipus-transference on his part, and . . .'

How tedious I found these phrases! We had come to the lake. I stooped over it and myself looked back at myself through the dark water. I looked at Dr. Gray's reflection and recognised her. I put on my dark glasses, then.

'Am I boring you?' she said.

'No, carry on.'

'Must you wear those glasses? . . . it is a modern psychological phenomenon . . . the trend towards impersonalisation . . . the modern Inquisitor.'

For a while, she watched her own footsteps as we walked round the lake. Then she continued her story. '. . . an optician. His sister was blind — *going* blind when I first attended her. Only the one eye was affected. Then there was an accident, one of those *psychological* accidents. She was a trained dispenser, but she mixed herself the wrong eye-drops. Now it's very difficult to make a mistake like that, normally. But subconsciously she wanted to, she *wanted* to. But she wasn't normal, she was not normal.'

'I'm not saying she was,' I said.

'What did you say?'

'I'm sure she wasn't a normal person,' I said, 'if you say so.'

'It can all be explained psychologically, as we've tried to show to my husband. We've told him and told him, and given him every sort of treatment — shock, insulin, everything. And after all, the stuff didn't have any effect on his sister immediately, and when she did go blind it was caused by acute glaucoma. She would probably have lost her sight in any case. Well, she went off her head completely and accused her brother of having put the wrong drug in the bottle deliberately. This is the interesting part from the psychological point of view — she said she had seen something that he didn't want her to see, something disreputable. She said he wanted to blind the eye that saw it. She said . . .'

We were walking round the lake for the second time. When we came to the spot where I had seen her face reflected I stopped and looked over the water.

'I'm boring you.'

'No, no.'

'I wish you would take off those glasses.'

I took them off for a moment. I rather liked her for her innocence in not recognising me, though she looked hard and said, 'There's a subconscious reason why you wear them.'

'Dark glasses hide dark thoughts,' I said.

'Is that a saying?'

'Not that I've heard. But it is one now.'

She looked at me anew. But she didn't recognise me.

These fishers of the mind have no eye for outward things. Instead, she was 'recognising' my mind: I daresay I came under some category of hers.

I had my glasses on again, and was walking on.

'How did your husband react to his sister's accusations?' I said.

'He was remarkably kind.'

'Kind?'

'Oh, yes, in the circumstances. Because she started up a lot of gossip in the neighbourhood. It was only a small town. It was a long time before I could persuade him to send her to a home for the blind where she could be looked after. There was a terrible bond between them. Unconscious incest.'

'Didn't you know that when you married him? I should have thought it would have been obvious.'

She looked at me again. 'I had not studied psychology at that time,' she said.

I thought, neither had I.

We were silent for the third turn about the lake. Then she said, 'Well, I was telling you how I came to study psychology and practise it. My husband had this breakdown after his sister went away. He had delusions. He kept imagining he saw eyes looking at him everywhere. He still sees them from time to time. But *eyes*, you see. That's significant. Unconsciously he felt he had blinded his sister. Because unconsciously he wanted to do so. He keeps confessing that he did so.'

'And attempted to forge the will?' I said.

She stopped. 'What are you saying?'

'Does he admit that he tried to forge his mother's will?'

'I haven't mentioned anything about a will.'

126

'Oh, I thought you had.'

'But, in fact, that was his sister's accusation. What made you say that? How did you know?'

'I must be psychic,' I said.

She took my arm. I had become a most endearing case history.

'You must be psychic indeed,' she said. 'You must tell me more about yourself. Well, that's the story of my taking up my present profession. When my husband started having these delusions and making these confessions I felt I had to understand the workings of the mind. And I began to study them. It has been fruitful. It has saved my own reason.'

'Did it ever occur to you that the sister's story might be true?' I said. 'Especially as he admits it.'

She took away her arm and said, 'Yes, I considered the possibility. I must admit I considered it well.'

She saw me watching her face. She looked as if she were pleading some personal excuse.

'Oh do,' she said, 'please take off those glasses.'

'Why don't you believe his own confession?'

'I'm a psychiatrist and we seldom believe confessions.' She looked at her watch as if to suggest I had started the whole conversation and was boring her.

I said, 'He might have stopped seeing eyes if you'd taken him at his word.'

She shouted, 'What are you saying? What are you thinking of? He wanted to give a statement to the police, do you realise . . .'

'You know he's guilty,' I said.

'As his wife,' she said, 'I know he's guilty. But as a psychiatrist I must regard him as innocent. That's why I took up the subject.' She suddenly turned angry and

127

shouted, 'You damned inquisitor, I've met your type before.'

I could hardly believe she was shouting, who previously had been so calm. 'Oh, it's not my business,' I said, and took off my glasses to show willing.

I think it was then she recognised me.

Bang-bang You're Dead

A<small>T</small> that time many of the men looked like Rupert Brooke, whose portrait still hung in everyone's imagination. It was that clear-cut, 'typically English' face which is seldom seen on the actual soil of England but proliferates in the African Colonies.

'I must say,' said Sybil's hostess, 'the men look charming.'

These men were all charming, Sybil had decided at the time, until you got to know them. She sat in the dark room watching the eighteen-year-old microfilm unrolling on the screen as if the particular memory had solidified under the effect of some intense heat coming out of the projector. She told herself, I was young, I demanded nothing short of perfection. But then, she thought, that is not quite the case. But it comes to the same thing; to me, the men were not charming for long.

The first reel came to an end. Someone switched on the light. Her host picked the next film out of its tropical packing.

'It must be an interesting experience,' said her hostess, 'seeing yourself after all those years.'

'Hasn't Sybil seen these films before?' said a late-comer.

'No, never — have you, Sybil?'

'No, never.'

'If they had been my films,' said her hostess, 'my curiosity could not have waited eighteen years.'

The Kodachrome reels had lain in their boxes in the dark of Sybil's cabin trunk. Why bother, when one's memory was clear?

'Sybil didn't know anyone who had a projector,' said her hostess, 'until we got ours.'

'It was delightful,' said the latecomer, an elderly lady, 'what I saw of it. Are the others as good?'

Sybil thought for a moment. 'The photography is probably good,' she said. 'There was a cook behind the camera.'

'A cook! How priceless; whatever do you mean?' said her hostess.

'The cook-boy,' said Sybil, 'was trained up to use the camera.'

'He managed it well,' said her host, who was adjusting the new reel.

'Wonderful colours,' said her hostess. 'Oh, I'm so glad you dug them out. How healthy and tanned and open-necked everyone looks. And those adorable shiny natives all over the place.'

The elderly lady said, 'I liked the bit where you came out on the verandah in your shorts carrying the gun.'

'Ready?' said Sybil's host. The new reel was fixed. 'Put out the lights,' he said.

It was the stoep again. Through the french windows came a dark girl in shorts followed by a frisky young Alsatian.

'Lovely dog,' commented Sybil's host. 'He seems to be asking Sybil for a game.'

'That is someone else,' Sybil said very quickly.

'The girl there, with the dog?'

'Yes, of course. Don't you see me walking across the lawn by the trees?'

'Oh, of course, of course. She did look like you, Sybil, that girl with the dog. Wasn't she like Sybil? I mean, just as she came out on the verandah.'

'Yes, *I* thought it was Sybil for a moment until I saw Sybil in the background. But you can see the difference now. See, as she turns round. That girl isn't really like Sybil, it must be the shorts.'

'There was a slight resemblance between us,' Sybil remarked.

The projector purred on.

'Look, there's a little girl rather like you, Sybil.' Sybil, walking between her mother and father, one hand in each, had already craned round. The other child, likewise being walked along, had looked back too.

The other child wore a black velour hat turned up all round, a fawn coat of covert-coating, and at her neck a narrow white ermine tie. She wore white silk gloves. Sybil was dressed identically, and though this in itself was nothing to marvel at, since numerous small girls wore this ensemble when they were walked out in the parks and public gardens of cathedral towns in 1923, it did fortify the striking resemblance in features, build, and height, between the two children. Sybil suddenly felt she was walking past her own reflection in the long looking-glass. There was her peak chin, her black bobbed hair under her hat, with its fringe almost touching her eyebrows. Her wide-spaced eyes, her nose very small like a cat's. 'Stop staring, Sybil,' whispered her mother. Sybil had time to snatch the gleam of white socks and black patent leather button shoes. Her own socks were white but her shoes were brown, with laces. At first she felt this one discrepancy was wrong, in the sense that it was wrong to step on one of the cracks in the pavement. Then she felt it was right that there should be a difference.

'The Colemans,' Sybil's mother remarked to her father. 'They keep that hotel at Hillend. The child must be about Sybil's age. Very alike, aren't they? And I suppose,' she continued for Sybil's benefit, 'she's a good little girl like Sybil.' Quick-witted Sybil thought poorly of the last remark with its subtle counsel of perfection.

On other occasions, too, they passed the Coleman child on a Sunday walk. In summer time the children wore panama hats and tussore silk frocks discreetly adorned with drawn-thread work. Sometimes the Coleman child was accompanied by a young maid-servant in grey dress and black stockings. Sybil noted this one difference between her own entourage and the other girl's. 'Don't turn round and stare,' whispered her mother.

It was not till she went to school that she found Désirée Coleman to be a year older than herself. Désirée was in a higher class but sometimes, when the whole school was assembled on the lawn or in the gym, Sybil would be, for a few moments, mistaken for Désirée. In the late warm spring the classes sat in separate groups under the plane trees until, as by simultaneous instinct, the teachers would indicate time for break. The groups would mingle, and 'Sybil, dear, your shoe-lace,' a teacher might call out; and then, as Sybil regarded her neat-laced shoes, 'Oh no, not Sybil,

I mean Désirée.' In the percussion band Sybil banged her triangle triumphantly when the teacher declared, '*Much* better than yesterday, Sybil.' But she added, 'I mean Désirée.'

Only the grown-ups mistook one child for another at odd moments. None of her small companions made this mistake. After the school concert Sybil's mother said, 'For a second I thought you were Désirée in the choir. It's strange you are so alike. I'm not a bit like Mrs. Coleman and your daddy doesn't resemble *him* in the least.'

Sybil found Désirée unsatisfactory as a playmate. Sybil was precocious, her brain was like a blade. She had discovered that dull children were apt to be spiteful. Désirée would sit innocently cross-legged beside you at a party, watching the conjurer, then suddenly, for no apparent reason, jab at you viciously with her elbow.

By the time Sybil was eight and Désirée nine it was seldom that anyone, even strangers and new teachers, mixed them up. Sybil's nose became more sharp and pronounced while Désirée's seemed to sink into her plump cheeks like a painted-on nose. Only on a few occasions, and only on dark winter afternoons between the last of three o'clock daylight and the coming on of lights all over the school, was Sybil mistaken for Désirée.

Between Sybil's ninth year and her tenth Désirée's family came to live in her square. The residents' children were taken to the gardens of the square after school by mothers and nursemaids, and were bidden to play with each other nicely. Sybil regarded the intrusion of Désirée sulkily, and said she preferred her book. She cheered up, however, when a few weeks later the Dobell boys came to live in the square. The two Dobells had dusky-rose skins and fine dark eyes. It appeared the father was half Indian.

How Sybil adored the Dobells! They were a new type of playmate in her experience, so jumping and agile, and yet so gentle, so unusually courteous. Their dark skins were never dirty, a fact which Sybil obscurely approved. She did not then mind Désirée joining in their games; the Dobell boys were a kind of charm against despair, for they did not understand stupidity and so did not notice Désirée's.

The girl lacked mental stamina, could not keep up an imaginative game for long, was shrill and apt to kick her playmates unaccountably and on the sly; the Dobells reacted to this with a simple resignation. Perhaps the lack of opposition was the reason that Désirée continually shot Sybil dead, contrary to the rules, whenever she felt like it.

Sybil resented with the utmost passion the repeated daily massacre of herself before the time was ripe. It was useless for Jon Dobell to explain, 'Not yet, Désirée. Wait, wait, Désirée. She's not to be shot down yet. She hasn't crossed the bridge yet, and you can't shoot her from there, anyway — there's a big boulder between you and her. You have to creep round it, and Hugh has a shot at you first, and he thinks he's got you, but only your hat. And . . .'

It was no use. Each day before the game started the four sat in conference on the short dry prickly grass. The proceedings were agreed. The game was on. 'Got it all clear, Désirée?' 'Yes,' she said, every day. Désirée shouted and got herself excited, she made foolish sounds even when supposed to be stalking the bandits through the silent forest. A few high screams and then, 'Bang-bang,' she yelled, aiming at Sybil, 'you're dead.' Sybil obediently rolled over, protesting none the less that the game had only begun, while the Dobells sighed, 'Oh, *Désirée!*'

Sybil vowed to herself each night, I will do the same to her. Next time — tomorrow if it isn't raining — I will bang-bang her before she has a chance to hang her panama on the bough as a decoy. I will say bang-bang on her out of turn, and I will do her dead before her time.

But on no succeeding tomorrow did Sybil bring herself to do this. Her pride before the Dobells was more valuable than the success of the game. Instead, with her cleverness, Sybil set herself to avoid Désirée's range for as long as possible. She dodged behind the laurels and threw out a running commentary as if to a mental defective, such as, 'I'm in disguise, all in green, and no one can see me among the trees.' But still Désirée saw her. Désirée's eyes insisted on penetrating solid mountains. 'I'm half a mile away from everyone,' Sybil cried as Désirée's gun swivelled relentlessly upon her.

I shall refuse to be dead, Sybil promised herself. I'll break the rule. If it doesn't count with her why should it count with me? I won't roll over any more when she bangs you're dead to me. Next time, tomorrow if it isn't raining . . .

But Sybil simply did roll over. When Jon and Hugh Dobell called out to her that Désirée's bang-bang did not count she started hopefully to resurrect herself; but 'It does count, it *does*. That's the rule,' Désirée counter-screeched. And Sybil dropped back flat, knowing utterly that this was final.

And so the girl continued to deal premature death to Sybil, losing her head, but never so much that she aimed at one of the boys. For some reason which Sybil did not consider until she was years and years older, it was always herself who had to die.

One day, when Désirée was late in arriving for play, Sybil put it to the boys that Désirée should be left out of the game in future. 'She only spoils it.'

'But,' said Jon, 'you need four people for the game.'

'You need four,' said Hugh.

'No, you can do it with three.' As she spoke she was inventing the game with three. She explained to them what was in her mind's eye. But neither boy could grasp the idea, having got used to Bandits and Riders with two on each side. 'I am the lone Rider, you see,' said Sybil. 'Or,' she wheedled, 'the cherry tree can be a Rider.' She was talking to stone, inoffensive but uncomprehending. All at once she realized, without articulating the idea, that her intelligence was superior to theirs, and she felt lonely.

'Could we play rounders instead?' ventured Jon.

Sybil brought a book every day after that, and sat reading beside her mother, who was glad, on the whole, that Sybil had grown tired of rowdy games.

'They were preparing,' said Sybil, 'to go on a shoot.'

Sybil's host was changing the reel.

'I get quite a new vision of Sybil,' said her hostess, 'seeing her in such a . . . such a *social* environment. Were any of these people intellectuals, Sybil?'

'No, but lots of poets.'

'Oh, *no*. Did they all write poetry?'

'Quite a lot of them,' said Sybil, 'did.'

'Who *were* they all? Who was that blond fellow who was standing by the van with you?'

'He was the manager of the estate. They grew passion-fruit and manufactured the juice.'

'Passion-fruit — how killing. Did *he* write poetry?'

'Oh, yes.'

'And who was the girl, the one I thought was you?'

'Oh, I had known her as a child and we met again in the Colony. The short man was her husband.'

'And were you all off on safari that morning? I simply can't imagine you shooting anything, Sybil, somehow.'

'On this occasion,' said Sybil, 'I didn't go. I just held the gun for effect.'

Everyone laughed.

'Do you still keep up with these people? I've heard that colonials are great letter writers, it keeps them in touch with——'

'No.' And she added, 'Three of them are dead. The girl and her husband, and the fair fellow.'

'Really? What happened to them? Don't tell me *they* were mixed up in shooting affairs.'

'They were mixed up in shooting affairs,' said Sybil.

'Oh, these colonials,' said the elderly woman, 'and their shooting affairs!'

'Number three,' said Sybil's host. 'Ready? Lights out, please.'

'Don't get eaten by lions. I say, Sybil, don't get mixed up in a shooting affair.' The party at the railway station were unaware of the noise they were making for they were inside the noise. As the time of departure drew near Donald's relatives tended to herd themselves apart while Sybil's clustered round the couple.

'Two years — it will be an interesting experience for them.'

'Mind out for the shooting affairs. Don't let Donald have a gun.'

There had been an outbreak of popular headlines about the shooting affairs in the Colony. Much had been blared forth about the effect, on the minds of young settlers, of the climate, the hard drinking, the shortage of white women. The Colony was a place where lovers shot husbands, or shot themselves, where husbands shot natives who spied through bedroom windows. Letters to *The Times* arrived belatedly from respectable colonists, refuting the scandals with sober statistics. The recent incidents, they said, did not represent the habits of the peaceable majority. The Governor told the press that everything had been highly exaggerated. By the time Sybil and Donald left for the Colony the music-hall comics had already exhausted the entertainment value of colonial shooting affairs.

'Don't make pets of snakes or crocs. Mind out for the lions. Don't forget to write.'

It was almost a surprise to them to find that shooting affairs in the Colony were not entirely a music-hall myth. They occurred in waves. For three months at a time the gun-murders and suicides were reported weekly. The old colonists with their very blue eyes sat beside their whisky bottles and remarked that another young rotter had shot himself. Then the rains would break and the shootings would cease for a long season.

Eighteen months after their marriage Donald was

mauled by a lioness and died on the long stretcher journey back to the station. He was one of a party of eight. No one could really say how it happened; it was done in a flash. The natives had lost their wits, and, instead of shooting the beast, had come calling 'Ah-ah-ah,' and pointing to the spot. A few strides, shouldering the grass aside, and Donald's friends got the lioness as she reared from his body.

His friends in the archaeological team to which he belonged urged Sybil to remain in the Colony for the remaining six months, and return to England with them. Still undecided, she went on a sight-seeing tour. But before their time was up the archaeologists had been recalled. War had been declared. Civilians were not permitted to leave the continent, and Sybil was caught, like Donald under the lioness.

She wished he had lived to enjoy a life of his own, as she intended to do. It was plain to her that they must have separated had he lived. There had been no disagreement but, thought Sybil, given another two years there would have been disagreements. Donald had shown signs of becoming a bore. By the last, the twenty-seventh, year of his life, his mind had ceased to enquire. Archaeology, that thrilling subject, had become Donald's job, merely. He began to talk as if all archaeological methods and theories had ceased to evolve on the day he obtained his degree; it was now only a matter of applying his knowledge to field-work for a limited period. Archaeological papers came out from England. The usual crank literature on roneo foolscap followed them from one postal address to another. 'Donald, aren't you going to look through them?' Sybil said, as the journals and papers piled up.

'No, really, I don't see it's necessary.' It was not necessary because his future was fixed; two years in the field and then a lectureship. If it were my subject, she thought, these papers would be necessary to me. Even the crackpot ones, rightly read, would be, to me, enlarging.

Sybil lay in bed in the mornings reading the translation of Kierkegaard's *Journals*, newly arrived from England in their first, revelatory month of publication. She felt like a desert which had not realised its own aridity till the rain began to fall upon it. When Donald came home in the late afternoons she had less and less to say to him.

'There has been another shooting affair,' Donald said, 'across the valley. The chap came home unexpectedly and found his wife with another man. He shot them both.'

'In this place, one is never far from the jungle,' Sybil said.

'What are you talking about? We are eight hundred miles from the jungle.'

When he had gone on his first big shoot, eight hundred miles away in the jungle, she had reflected, there is no sign of a living mind in him, it is like a landed fish which has ceased to palpitate. But, she thought, another woman would never notice it. Other women do not wish to be married to a Mind. Yet I do, she thought, and I am a freak and should not have married. In fact I am not the marrying type. Perhaps that is why he does not explore my personality, any more than he reads the journals. It might make him think, and that would be hurtful.

After his death she wished he had lived to enjoy a

life of his own, whatever that might have been. She
took a job in a private school for girls and cultivated a
few friends for diversion until the war should be over.
Charming friends need not possess minds.

Their motor launch was rocking up the Zambezi.
Sybil was leaning over the rail mouthing something to a
startled native in a canoe. Now Sybil was pointing
across the river.

'I think I was asking him,' Sybil commented to her
friends in the darkness, 'about the hippo. There was a
school of hippo some distance away, and we wanted to
see them better. But the native said we shouldn't go too
near — that's why he's looking so frightened — because
the hippo often upset a boat, and then the crocs quickly
slither into the water. There, look! We got a long shot
of the hippo — those bumps in the water, like sub-
marines, those are the snouts of hippo.'

The film rocked with the boat as it proceeded up the
river. The screen went white.

'Something's happened,' said Sybil's hostess.

'Put on the light,' said Sybil's host. He fiddled with
the projector and a young man, their lodger from upstairs, went to help him.

'I loved those tiny monkeys on the island,' said her
hostess. 'Do hurry, Ted. What's gone wrong?'

'Shut up a minute,' he said.

'Sybil, you know you haven't changed much since
you were a girl.'

'Thank you, Ella.' I haven't changed at all so far as
I still think charming friends need not possess minds.

'I expect this will revive your memories, Sybil. The
details, I mean. One is bound to forget so much.'

'Oh yes,' Sybil said, and she added, 'but I recall quite a lot of details, you know.'

'Do you *really*, Sybil?'

I wish, she thought, they wouldn't cling to my least word.

The young man turned from the projector with several feet of the film-strip looped between his wide-spread hands. 'Is the fair chap your husband, Mrs. Greeves?' he said to Sybil.

'Sybil lost her husband very early on,' her hostess informed him in a low and sacred voice.

'Oh, I *am* sorry.'

Sybil's hostess replenished the drinks of her three guests. Her host turned from the projector, finished his drink, and passed his glass to be refilled, all in one movement. Everything they do seems large and important, thought Sybil, but I must not let it be so. We are only looking at old films.

She overheard a sibilant 'Whish-sh-sh?' from the elderly woman in which she discerned, 'Who is she?'

'Sybil Greeves,' her hostess breathed back, 'a distant cousin of Ted's through marriage.'

'Oh yes?' The low tones were puzzled as if all had not been explained.

'She's quite famous, of course.'

'Oh, I didn't know that.'

'Very few people know it,' said Sybil's hostess with a little arrogance.

'O.K.,' said Ted, 'lights out.'

'I must say,' said his wife, 'the colours are marvellous.'

All the time she was in the Colony Sybil longed for the inexplicable colourings of her native land. The flamboyants were too rowdy, the birds, the native women with their heads bound in cloth of piercing pink, their blinding black skin and white teeth, the baskets full of bright tough flowers or oranges on their heads, the sight of which everyone else admired ('How I wish I could paint all this!') distressed Sybil, it bored her.

She rented a house, sharing it with a girl whose husband was fighting in the north. She was twenty-two. To safeguard her privacy absolutely, she had a plywood partition put up in the sitting-room, for it was another ten years before she had learnt those arts of leading a double life and listening to people ambiguously, which enabled her to mix without losing identity, and to listen without boredom.

On the other side of the partition Ariadne Lewis decorously entertained her friends, most of whom were men on leave. On a few occasions Sybil attended these parties, working herself, as in a frenzy of self-discipline, into a state of carnal excitement over the men. She managed to do this only by an effortful sealing-off of all her critical faculties except those which assessed a good male voice and appearance. The hangovers were frightful.

The scarcity of white girls made it easy for any one of them to keep a number of men in perpetual attendance. Ariadne had many boy friends but no love affairs. Sybil had three affairs in the space of two years, to put herself to the test. They started at private dances, in the magnolia-filled gardens that smelt like a scent factory, under the Milky Way which looked like an overcrowded jeweller's window. The affairs ended when she succumbed to one of her attacks of tropical 'flu, and lay in a twilight of the senses on a bed which had been set on the stone stoep and overhung with a white mosquito net like something bridal. With damp shaky hands she would write a final letter to the man and give it to her half-caste maid to post. He would telephone next morning, and would be put off by the house boy, who was quite intelligent.

For some years she had been thinking she was not much inclined towards sex. After the third affair, this dawned and rose within her as a whole realization, as if in the past, when she had told herself, 'I am not predominantly a sexual being,' or 'I'm rather a frigid freak, I suppose,' these were the sayings of an illiterate, never quite rational and known until now, but after the third affair the notion was so intensely conceived as to be almost new. It appalled her. She lay on the shady stoep, her fever subsiding, and examined her relations with men. She thought, what if I married again? She shivered under the hot sheet. Can it be, she thought, that I have a suppressed tendency towards women? She lay still and let the idea probe round in imagination. She surveyed, with a stony inward eye, all the women she had known, prim little academicians with cream peter-pan collars on their dresses, large dominant women, a number of beauties, conventional nitwits like Ariadne. No, really, she thought; neither men nor women. It is a not caring for sexual relations. It is not merely a lack of pleasure in sex, it is dislike of the excitement. And it is not merely dislike, it is worse, it is boredom.

She felt a lonely emotion near to guilt. The three love affairs took on heroic aspects in her mind. They were an attempt, thought Sybil, to do the normal thing.

Perhaps I may try again. Perhaps, if I should meet the right man . . . But at the idea 'right man' she felt a sense of intolerable desolation and could not stop shivering. She raised the mosquito net and reached for the lemon juice, splashing it jerkily into the glass. She sipped. The juice had grown warm and had been made too sweet, but she let it linger on her sore throat and peered through the net at the backs of houses and the yellow veldt beyond them.

Ariadne said one morning, 'I met a girl last night, it was funny. I thought it was you at first and called over to her. But she wasn't really like you close up, it was just an impression. As a matter of fact, she knows you. I've asked her to tea. I forget her name.'

'I don't,' said Sybil.

But when Désirée arrived they greeted each other with exaggerated warmth, wholly felt at the time, as acquaintances do when they meet in another hemisphere. Sybil had last seen Désirée at a dance in Hampstead, and there had merely said, 'Oh, hallo.'

'We were at our first school together,' Désirée explained to Ariadne, still holding Sybil's hand.

Already Sybil wished to withdraw. 'It's strange,' she remarked, 'how, sooner or later, everyone in the Colony meets someone they have known, or their parents knew, at home.'

Désirée and her husband, Barry Weston, were settled in a remote part of the Colony. Sybil had heard of Weston, unaware that Désirée was his wife. He was much talked of as an enterprising planter. Some years ago he had got the idea of manufacturing passion-fruit juice, had planted orchards and set up a factory. The business was now expanding wonderfully. Barry Weston also wrote poetry, a volume of which, entitled *Home Thoughts*, he had published and sold with great success within the confines of the Colony. His first wife had died of blackwater fever. On one of his visits to England he had met and married Désirée, who was twelve years his junior.

'You *must* come and see us,' said Désirée to Sybil; and to Ariadne she explained again, 'We were at our first little private school together.' And she said, 'Oh, Sybil, do you remember Trotsky? Do you remember Minnie Mouse, what a hell of a life we gave her? I shall never forget that day when . . .'

The school where Sybil taught was shortly to break up for holidays; Ariadne was to visit her husband in Cairo at that time. Sybil promised a visit to the Westons. When Désirée, beautifully dressed in linen suiting, had departed, Ariadne said, 'I'm so glad you're going to stay with them. I hated the thought of your being all alone for the next few weeks.'

'Do you know,' Sybil said, 'I don't think I shall go to stay with them after all. I'll make an excuse.'

'Oh, why not? Oh, Sybil, it's such a lovely place, and it will be fun for you. He's a poet, too.' Sybil could sense exasperation, could hear Ariadne telling her friends, 'There's something wrong with Sybil. You never know a person till you live with them. Now Sybil will say one thing one minute, and the next . . . Something wrong with her sex-life, perhaps . . . odd . . .'

At home, thought Sybil, it would not be such a slur. Her final appeal for a permit to travel to England had just been dismissed. The environment mauled her weakness. 'I think I'm going to have a cold,' she said, shivering.

'Go straight to bed, dear.' Ariadne called for black Elijah and bade him prepare some lemon juice. But the cold did not materialize.

She returned with 'flu, however, from her first visit to the Westons. Her 1936 Ford V8 had broken down on the road and she had waited three chilly hours before another car had appeared.

'You must get a decent car,' said the chemist's wife, who came to console her. 'These old crocks simply won't stand up to the roads out here.'

Sybil shivered and held her peace. Nevertheless, she returned to the Westons at mid-term.

Désirée's invitations were pressing, almost desperate. Again and again Sybil went in obedience to them. The Westons were a magnetic field.

There was a routine attached to her arrival. The elegant wicker chair was always set for her in the same position on the stoep. The same cushions, it seemed, were always piled in exactly the same way.

'What will you drink, Sybil? Are you comfy there, Sybil? We're going to give you a wonderful time, Sybil.' She was their little orphan, she supposed. She sat, with very dark glasses, contemplating the couple. 'We've planned — haven't we, Barry? — a surprise for you, Sybil.' 'We've planned — haven't we, Désirée? — a marvellous trip . . . a croc hunt . . . hippo . . .'

Sybil sips her gin and lime. Facing her on the wicker sofa, Désirée and her husband sit side by side. They gaze at Sybil affectionately. 'Take off your smoke glasses, Sybil, the sun's nearly gone.' Sybil takes them off. The couple hold hands. They peck kisses at each other, and presently, outrageously, they are entwined in a long erotic embrace in the course of which Barry once or twice regards Sybil from the corner of his eye. Barry disengages himself and sits with his arm about his wife; she snuggles up to him. Why, thinks Sybil, is this performance being staged? 'Sybil is shocked,' Barry remarks. She sips her drink, and reflects that a public display between man and wife somehow is more shocking than are courting couples in parks and doorways. 'We're very much in love with each other,' Barry explains, squeezing his wife. And Sybil wonders what is wrong with their marriage since obviously something is wrong. The couple kiss again. Am I dreaming this? Sybil asks herself.

Even on her first visit Sybil knew definitely there was something wrong with the marriage. She thought of herself, at first, as an objective observer, and was even amused when she understood they had chosen her to be their sort of Victim of Expiation. On occasions when other guests were present she noted that the love scenes did not take place. Instead, the couple tended to snub Sybil before their friends. 'Poor little Sybil, she lives all alone and is a teacher, and hasn't many friends. We have her here to stay as often as possible.' The people would look uneasily at Sybil, and would smile. 'But you must have *heaps* of friends,' they would say politely. Sybil came to realize she was an object of the Westons' resentment, and that, nevertheless, they found her indispensable.

Ariadne returned from Cairo. 'You always look washed out when you've been staying at the Westons,' she told Sybil eventually. 'I suppose it's due to the late parties and lots of drinks.'

'I suppose so.'

Désirée wrote continually. 'Do come, Barry needs you. He needs your advice about some sonnets.' Sybil tore up these letters quickly, but usually went. Not because her discomfort was necessary to their wellbeing, but because it was somehow necessary to her own. The act of visiting the Westons alleviated her sense of guilt.

I believe, she thought, they must discern my abnormality. How could they have guessed? She was always cautious when they dropped questions about her private life. But one's closest secrets have a subtle way of communicating themselves to the resentful vigilance of opposite types. I do believe, she thought, that heart speaks unto heart, and deep calleth unto deep. But rarely in clear language. There is a misunderstanding here. They imagine their demonstrations of erotic bliss will torment my frigid soul, and so far they are right. But the reason for my pain is not envy. Really, it is boredom.

Her Ford V8 rattled across country. How bored, she thought, I am going to be by their married tableau! How pleased, exultant, they will be! These thoughts consoled her, they were an offering to the gods.

'Are you comfy, Sybil?'

She sipped her gin and lime. 'Yes, thanks.'

His pet name for Désirée was Dearie. 'Kiss me, Dearie,' he said.

'There, Baddy,' his wife said to Barry, snuggling close to him and squinting at Sybil.

'I say, Sybil,' Barry said as he smoothed down his hair, 'you ought to get married again. You're missing such a lot.'

'Yes, Sybil,' said Désirée, 'you should either marry or enter a convent, one or the other.'

'I don't see why,' Sybil said, 'I should fit into a tidy category.'

'Well, you're neither one thing nor another — is she, honeybunch?'

True enough, thought Sybil, and that is why I'm laid out on the altar of boredom.

'Or get yourself a boy-friend,' said Désirée. 'It would be good for you.'

'You're wasting your best years,' said Barry.

'Are you comfy there, Sybil? . . . We want you to enjoy yourself here. Any time you want to bring a boy friend, we're broadminded — aren't we, Baddy?'

'Kiss me, Dearie,' he said.

Désirée took his handkerchief from his pocket and rubbed lipstick from his mouth. He jerked his head away and said to Sybil, 'Pass your glass.'

Désirée looked at her reflection in the glass of the french windows and said, 'Sybil's too intellectual, that's her trouble.' She patted her hair, then looked at Sybil with an old childish enmity.

After dinner Barry would read his poems. Usually, he said, 'I'm not going to be an egotist tonight. I'm not going to read my poems.' And usually Désirée would cry, 'Oh do, Barry, do.' Always, eventually, he did. 'Marvellous,' Désirée would comment, 'wonderful.' By the third night of her visits, the farcical aspect of it all would lose its fascination for Sybil, and boredom would fill her near to bursting point, like gas in a balloon. To relieve the strain, she would sigh deeply from time to time. Barry was too engrossed in his own voice to notice this, but Désirée was watching. At first Sybil worded her comments tactfully. 'I think you should devote more of your time to your verses,' she said. And, since he looked puzzled, added, 'You owe it to poetry if you write it.'

'Nonsense,' said Désirée, 'he often writes a marvellous sonnet before shaving in the morning.'

'Sybil may be right,' said Barry. 'I owe poetry all the time I can give.'

'Are you tired, Sybil?' said Désirée. 'Why are you sighing like that; are you all right?'

Later, Sybil gave up the struggle and wearily said, 'Very good,' or 'Nice rhythm' after each poem. And even the guilt of condoning Désirée's 'marvellous . . . wonderful' was less than the guilt of her isolated mind. She did not know then that the price of allowing false opinions was the gradual loss of one's capacity for forming true ones.

Not every morning, but at least twice during each visit Sybil would wake to hear the row in progress. The nanny, who brought her early tea, made large eyes and tiptoed warily. Sybil would have her bath, splashing a lot to drown the noise of the quarrel. Downstairs, the battle of voices descended, filled every room and corridor. When, on the worst occasions, the sound of shattering glass broke through the storm, Sybil would know that Barry was smashing up Désirée's dressing table; and would wonder how Désirée always managed to replace her crystal bowls, since goods of that type were now scarce, and why she bothered to do so. Sybil would always find the two girls of Barry's former marriage standing side by side on the lawn frankly gazing up at the violent bedroom window. The nanny would cart off Désirée's baby for a far-away walk. Sybil would likewise disappear for the morning.

The first time this happened, Désirée told her later, 'I'm afraid you unsettle Barry.'

'What do you mean?' said Sybil.

Désirée dabbed her watery eyes and blew her nose. 'Well, of *course*, it stands to reason, Sybil, you're out to attract Barry. And he's only a man. I know you do it *unconsciously*, but . . .'

'I can't stand this sort of thing. I shall leave right away,' Sybil said.

'No, Sybil, no. Don't make a *thing* of it. Barry needs you. You're the only person in the Colony who can really talk to him about his poetry.'

'Understand,' said Sybil on that first occasion, 'I am not at all interested in your husband. I think he's an all-round third-rater. That is my opinion.'

Désirée looked savage. 'Barry,' she shouted, 'has made a fortune out of passion-fruit juice in eight years. He has sold four thousand copies of *Home Thoughts* on his own initiative.'

It was like a game for three players. According to the rules, she was to be in love, unconsciously, with Barry, and tortured by the contemplation of Désirée's married bliss. She felt too old to join in, just at that moment.

Barry came to her room while she was packing. 'Don't go,' he said. 'We need you. And after all, we are only human. What's a row? These quarrels only happen in the best marriages. And I can't for the life of me think how it started.'

'What a beautiful house. What a magnificent estate,' said Sybil's hostess.

'Yes,' said Sybil, 'it was the grandest in the Colony.'

'Were the owners frightfully grand?'

'Well, they were rich, of course.'

'I can see that. What a beautiful interior. I adore those lovely old oil lamps. I suppose you didn't have electricity?'

'Yes, there was electric light in all the rooms. But my friends preferred the oil-lamp tradition for the dining-room. You see, it was a copy of an old Dutch house.'

'Absolutely charming.'

The reel came to an end. The lights went up and everyone shifted in their chairs.

'What were those large red flowers?' said the elderly lady.

'Flamboyants.'

'Magnificent,' said her hostess. 'Don't you miss the colours, Sybil?'

'No, I don't, actually. There was too much of it for me.'

'You didn't care for the bright colours?' said the young man, leaning forward eagerly.

Sybil smiled at him.

'I liked the bit where those little lizards were playing among the stones. That was an excellent shot,' said her host. He was adjusting the last spool.

'I rather *liked* that handsome blond fellow,' said her hostess, as if the point had been in debate. 'Was he the passion-fruiter?'

'He was the manager,' said Sybil.

'Oh yes, you told me. He was in a shooting affair, did you say?'

'Yes, it was unfortunate.'

'Poor young man. It sounds quite a dangerous place. I suppose the sun and everything . . .'

'It was dangerous for some people. It depended.'

'The blacks look happy enough. Did you have any trouble with them in those days?'

'No,' said Sybil, 'only with the whites.'

Everyone laughed.

'Right,' said her host. 'Lights out, please.'

Sybil soon perceived the real cause of the Westons' quarrels. It differed from their explanations: they were both, they said, so much in love, so jealous of each other's relations with the opposite sex.

'Barry was furious,' said Désirée one day, '— weren't you, Barry? — because I smiled, merely smiled, at Carter.'

'I'll have it out with Carter,' muttered Barry. 'He's always hanging round Désirée.'

David Carter was their manager. Sybil was so foolish as once to say, 'Oh surely David wouldn't——'

'Oh wouldn't he?' said Désirée.

'Oh wouldn't he?' said Barry.

Possibly they did not themselves know the real cause of their quarrels. These occurred on mornings when Barry had decided to lounge in bed and write poetry. Désirée, anxious that the passion-fruit business should continue to expand, longed for him to be at his office in the factory at eight o'clock each morning, by which time all other enterprising men in the Colony were at work. But Barry spoke more and more of retiring and devoting his time to his poems. When he lay abed, pen in hand, worrying a sonnet, Désirée would sulk and bang doors. The household knew that the row was on.

'Quiet! Don't you see I'm trying to think,' he would shout. '*I* suggest,' she would reply, 'you go to the library if you want to write.' It was evident that her greed and his vanity, facing each other in growling antipathy, were too terrible for either to face. Instead, the names of David Carter and Sybil would fly between them, consoling them, pepping-up and propagating the myth of their mutual attraction.

'Rolling your eyes at Carter in the orchard. Don't think I didn't notice.'

'Carter? That's funny. I can easily keep Carter in his place. But while we're on the subject, what about you with Sybil? You sat up late enough with her last night after I'd gone to bed.'

Sometimes he not only smashed the crystal bowls, he hurled them through the window.

In the exhausted afternoon Barry would explain, 'Désirée was upset — weren't you, Désirée? — because of you, Sybil. It's understandable. We shouldn't stay up late talking after Désirée has gone to bed. You're a little devil in your way, Sybil.'

'Oh well,' said Sybil obligingly, 'that's how it is.'

She became tired of the game. When, in the evenings, Barry's voice boomed forth with sonorous significance as befits a hallowed subject, she no longer thought of herself as an objective observer. She had tired of the game because she was now more than nominally committed to it. She ceased to be bored by the Westons; she began to hate them.

'What I don't understand,' said Barry, 'is why my poems are ignored back in England. I've sold over four thousand of the book out here. Feature articles about me have appeared in all the papers out here; remind me to show you them. But I can't get a single notice in London. When I send a poem to any of the magazines I don't even get a reply.'

'They are engaged in a war,' Sybil said.

'But they still publish poetry. Poetry so-called. Utter rubbish, all of it. You can't understand the stuff.'

'Yours is too good for them,' said Sybil. To a delicate ear her tone might have resembled the stab of a pin stuck into a waxen image.

'That's a fact, between ourselves,' said Barry. 'I shouldn't say it, but that's the answer.'

Barry was over-weight, square and dark. His face had lines, as of anxiety or stomach trouble. David Carter, when he passed, cool and fair through the house, was quite a change.

'England is finished,' said Barry. 'It's degenerate.'

'I wonder,' said Sybil, 'you have the heart to go on writing so cheerily about the English towns and countryside.' Now, now, Sybil, she thought; business is business, and the nostalgic English scene is what the colonists want. This visit must be my last. I shall not come again.

'Ah, that,' Barry was saying, 'was the England I remember. The good old country. But now, I'm afraid, it's decadent. After the war it will be no more than . . .'

Désirée would have the servants into the drawing-room every morning to give them their orders for the day. 'I believe in keeping up home standards,' said Désirée, whose parents were hotel managers. Sybil was not sure where Désirée had got the idea of herding all the domestics into her presence each morning. Perhaps it was some family-prayer assembly in her ancestral memory, or possibly it had been some hotel-staff custom which prompted her to 'have in the servants' and instruct them beyond their capacity. These half-domesticated peasants and erstwhile small-farmers stood, barefooted and woolly-cropped, in clumsy postures on Désirée's carpet. In pidgin dialect which they largely failed to comprehend, she enunciated the duties of each one. Only Sybil and David Carter knew that the natives' name for Désirée was, translated, 'Bad Hen'. Désirée complained much about their stupidity, but she enjoyed this morning palaver as Barry relished his poetry.

'Carter writes poetry too,' said Barry with a laugh one day.

Désirée shrieked. 'Poetry! Oh, Barry, you can't call that stuff *poetry*.'

'It is frightful,' Barry said, 'but the poor fellow doesn't know it.'

'I should like to see it,' Sybil said.

'You aren't interested in Carter by any chance, Sybil?' said Désirée.

'How do you mean?'

'Personally, I mean.'

'Well, I think he's all right.'

'Be honest, Sybil,' said Barry. Sybil felt extremely irritated. He so often appealed for frankness in others, as if by right; was so dishonest with himself. 'Be honest, Sybil — you're after David Carter.'

'He's handsome,' Sybil said.

'You haven't a chance,' said Barry. 'He's mad keen on Désirée. And anyway, Sybil, you don't want a beginner.'

'You want a mature man in a good position,' said

Désirée. 'The life you're living isn't natural for a girl. I've been noticing,' she said, 'you and Carter being matey together out on the farm.'

Towards the end of her stay David Carter produced his verses for Sybil to read. She thought them interesting but unpractised. She told him so, and was disappointed that he did not take this as a reasonable criticism. He was very angry. 'Of course,' she said, 'your poetry is far better than Barry's.' This failed to appease David. After a while, when she was meeting him in the town where she lived, she began to praise his poems, persuading herself that he was fairly talented.

She met him whenever he could get away. She sent excuses in answer to Désirée's pressing invitations. For different reasons, both Sybil and David were anxious to keep their meetings secret from the Westons. Sybil did not want the affair mythologized and gossiped about. For David's part, he valued his job in the flourishing passion-fruit concern. He had confided to Sybil his hope, one day, to have the whole business under his control. He might even buy Barry out. 'I know far more about it than he does. He's getting more and more bound up with his poetry, and paying next to no attention to the business. I'm just waiting.' He is, Sybil remarked to herself on hearing this, a true poet all right.

David reported that the quarrels between Désirée and Barry were becoming more violent, that the possibility of Barry's resigning from business to devote his time to poetry was haunting Désirée. 'Why don't you come,' Désirée wrote, 'and talk to Barry about his poetry? Why don't you come and see us now? What have we done? Poor Sybil, all alone in the world, you ought to be married. David Carter follows me all over the place, it's most embarrassing, you know how furious Barry gets. Well, I suppose that's the cost of having a devoted husband.' Perhaps, thought Sybil, she senses that David is my lover.

One day she went down with 'flu. David turned up unexpectedly and proposed marriage. He clung to her with violent, large hands. She alone, he said, understood his ambitions, his art, himself. Within a year or two they could, together, take over the passion-fruit plantation.

'Sh-sh. Ariadne will hear you.' Ariadne was out, in fact. David looked at her somewhat wildly. 'We must be married,' he said.

Sybil's affair with David Carter was over, from her point of view, almost before it had started. She had engaged in it as an act of virtue done against the grain, and for a brief time it had absolved her from the reproach of her sexlessness.

'I'm waiting for an answer.' By his tone, he seemed to suspect what the answer would be.

'Oh, David, I was just about to write to you. We really must put an end to this. As for marriage, well, I'm not cut out for it at all.'

He stooped over her bed and clung to her. 'You'll catch my 'flu,' she said. 'I'll think about it,' she said, to get rid of him.

When he had gone she wrote him her letter, sipping lemon juice to ease her throat. She noticed he had brought for her, and left on the floor of the stoep, six bottles of Weston's Passion-fruit Juice. He will soon get over the affair, she thought, he has still got his obsession with the passion-fruit business.

But in response to her letter David forced his way into

the house. Sybil was alarmed. None of her previous lovers had persisted in this way.

'It's your duty to marry me.'

'Really, what next?'

'It's your duty to me as a man and a poet.' She did not like his eyes.

'As a poet,' she said, 'I think you're a third-rater.' She felt relieved to hear her own voice uttering the words.

He stiffened up in a comical melodramatic style, looking such a clean-cut settler with his golden hair and tropical suiting.

'David Carter,' wrote Désirée, 'has gone on the bottle. I think he's bats, myself. It's because I keep giving him the brush-off. Isn't it all silly? The estate will go to ruin if Barry doesn't get rid of him. Barry has sent him away on leave for a month, but if he hasn't improved on his return we shall have to make a change. When are you coming? Barry needs to talk to you.'

Sybil went the following week, urged on by her old self-despising; driving her Ford V8 against the current of pleasure, yet compelled to expiate her abnormal nature by contact with the Westons' sexuality, which she knew, none the less, would bore her.

They twisted the knife within an hour of her arrival.

'Haven't you found a man yet?' said Barry.

'You ought to try a love affair,' said Désirée. 'We've been saying — haven't we, Barry? — you ought to, Sybil. It would be good for you. It isn't healthy, the life you lead. That's why you get 'flu so often. It's psychological.'

'Come out on the lawn,' Barry had said when she

first arrived. 'We've got the ciné camera out. Come and be filmed.'

Désirée said, 'Carter came back this morning.'

'Oh, is he here? I thought he was away for a month.'

'So did we. But he turned up this morning.'

'He's moping,' Barry said, 'about Désirée. She snubs him so badly.'

'He's psychological,' said Désirée.

'I love that striped awning,' said Sybil's hostess. 'It puts the finishing touch on the whole scene. How carefree you all look — don't they, Ted?'

'*That* chap looks miserable,' Ted observed. He referred to a shot of David Carter who had just ambled within range of the camera.

Everyone laughed, for David looked exceedingly grim.

'He was caught in an off-moment there,' said Sybil's hostess. 'Oh, there goes Sybil. I thought you looked a little sad just then, Sybil. There's that other girl again, and the lovely dog.'

'Was this a *typical* afternoon in the Colony?' enquired the young man.

'It was and it wasn't,' Sybil said.

Whenever they had the camera out life changed at the Westons. Everyone, including the children, had to look very happy. The house natives were arranged to appear in the background wearing their best whites. Sometimes Barry would have everyone dancing in a ring with the children, and the natives had to clap time.

Or, as on the last occasion, he would stage an effect

of gracious living. The head cook-boy, who had a good
knowledge of photography, was placed at his post.

'Ready,' said Barry to the cook, 'shoot.'

Désirée came out, followed by the dog.

'Look frisky, Barker,' said Barry. The Alsatian
looked frisky.

Barry put one arm round Désirée and his other arm
through Sybil's that late afternoon, walking them
slowly across the camera range. He chatted with
amiability and with an actor's lift of the head. He
would accentuate his laughter, tossing back his head.
A sound track would, however, have reproduced the
words, 'Smile, Sybil. Walk slowly. Look as if you're
enjoying it. You'll be able to see yourself in later years,
having the time of your life.'

Sybil giggled.

Just then David was seen to be securing the little
lake boat between the trees. 'He must have come across
the lake,' said Barry. 'I wonder if he's been drinking
again?'

But David's walk was quite steady. He did not
realise he was being photographed as he crossed the
long lawn. He stood for a moment staring at Sybil.
She said, 'Oh hallo, David.' He turned and walked
aimlessly face-on towards the camera.

'Hold it a minute,' Barry called out to the cook.

The boy obeyed at the moment David realized he had
been filmed.

'O.K.,' shouted Barry, when David was out of range.
'Fire ahead.'

It was then Barry said to Sybil, 'Haven't you found
a man yet . . .?' and Désirée said, 'You ought to try a
love affair. . . .'

'We've made Sybil unhappy,' said Désirée.

'Oh, I'm quite happy.'

'Well, cheer up in front of the camera,' said Barry.

The sun was setting fast, the camera was folded away, and everyone had gone to change. Sybil came down and sat on the stoep outside the open french windows of the dining-room. Presently, Désirée was indoors behind her, adjusting the oil lamps which one of the house-boys had set too high. Désirée put her head round the glass door and remarked to Sybil, 'That Benjamin's a fool, I shall speak to him in the morning. He simply will not take care with these lamps. One day we'll have a real smoke-out.'

Sybil said, 'Oh, I expect they are all so used to electricity these days. . . .'

'That's the trouble,' said Désirée, and turned back into the room.

Sybil was feeling disturbed by David's presence in the place. She wondered if he would come in to dinner. Thinking of his sullen staring at her on the lawn, she felt he might make a scene. She heard a gasp from the dining-room behind her.

She looked round, but in the same second it was over. A deafening crack from the pistol and Désirée crumpled up. A movement by the inner door and David held the gun to his head. Sybil screamed, and was aware of running footsteps upstairs. The gun exploded again and David's body dropped sideways.

With Barry and the natives she went round to the dining-room. Désirée was dead. David lingered a moment enough to roll his eyes in Sybil's direction as she rose from Désirée's body. He knows, thought Sybil quite lucidly, that he got the wrong woman.

'What I can't understand,' said Barry when he called on Sybil a few weeks later, 'is why he did it.'

'He was mad,' said Sybil.

'Not all that mad,' said Barry. 'And everyone thinks, of course, that there was an affair between them. That's what I can't bear.'

'Quite,' said Sybil. 'But of course he was keen on Désirée. You always said so. Those rows you used to have. . . . You always made out you were jealous of David.'

'Do you know,' he said, 'I wasn't, really. It was a sort of . . . a sort of . . .'

'Play-act,' said Sybil.

'Sort of. You see, there was nothing between them,' he said, 'And honestly, Carter wasn't a bit interested in Désirée. And the question is *why* he did it. I can't bear people to think . . .'

The damage to his pride, Sybil saw, outweighed his grief. The sun was setting and she rose to put on the stoep light.

'Stop!' he said. 'Turn round. My God, you did look like Désirée for a moment.'

'You're nervy,' she said, and switched on the light.

'In some ways you *do* look a little like Désirée,' he said. 'In some lights,' he said reflectively.

I must say something, thought Sybil, to blot this notion from his mind. I must make this occasion un-memorable, distasteful to him.

'At all events,' she said, 'you've still got your poetry.'

'That's the great thing,' he said, 'I've still got that. It means everything to me, a great consolation. I'm selling up the estate and joining up. The kids are going into a convent and I'm going up north. What we need is some good war poetry. There hasn't been any war poetry.'

'You'll make a better soldier,' she said, 'than a poet.'

'What do you say?'

She repeated her words fairly slowly, and with a sense of relief, almost of absolution. The season of falsity had formed a scab, soon to fall away altogether. There is no health, she thought, for me, outside of honesty.

'You've always,' he said, 'thought my poetry was wonderful.'

'I have said so,' she said, 'but it was a sort of play-act. Of course, it's only my opinion, but I think you're a third-rater poet.'

'You're upset, my dear,' he said.

He sent her the four reels of film from Cairo a month before he was killed in action. 'It will be nice in later years,' he wrote, 'for you to recall those good times we used to have.'

'It has been delightful,' said her hostess. 'You haven't changed a bit. Do you *feel* any different?'

'Well yes, I feel rather differently about everything, of course.' One learns to accept oneself.

'A hundred feet of one's past life!' said the young man. 'If they were mine, I'm sure I should be shattered. I should be calling "Lights! Lights!" like Hamlet's uncle.'

Sybil smiled at him. He looked back, suddenly solemn and shrewd.

'How tragic, those people being killed in shooting affairs,' said the elderly woman.

'The last reel was the best,' said her hostess. 'The garden was entrancing. I should like to see that one again; what about you, Ted?'

'Yes, I liked those nature-study shots. I feel I missed a lot of it,' said her husband.

'Hark at him — nature-study shots!'

'Well, those close-ups of tropical plants.'

Everyone wanted the last one again.

'How about you, Sybil?'

Am I a woman, she thought calmly, or an intellectual monster? She was so accustomed to this question within herself that it needed no answer. She said, 'Yes, I should like to see it again. It's an interesting experience.'

The Interview

CAST

Dame Lettice
Miss Bone ('Tiggy')
Roy

(*The scene is a large flat off Knightsbridge, the abode of Dame Lettice Chatterton, who was well known in political circles during the 'twenties; of her companion-secretary, Miss Bone; and, intermittently, of her nephew, Roy, a theological student. It is late afternoon in winter*)

Lettice. Why don't you get your teeth seen to, Tiggy? They look terrible.

Tiggy. It's raining again.

Lettice. I always think that's one of the most important things about a woman, her teeth.

Tiggy. It says rain continuing well into the afternoon, temperature slightly above average.

Lettice. How far had we got?

Tiggy. 'My personality . . .'

Lettice. Oh, Tiggy, read the whole sentence.

Tiggy. 'It has therefore always been difficult for me, with so many sides to my personality . . .'

(*Pause*)

Lettice. Go on, continue.

Tiggy. You didn't finish the sentence.

Lettice. I'm sure I did.

Tiggy. I'm sure you are.

Lettice. It has therefore always been difficult for me comma with so many sides to my personality comma to present only one of those sides at any one time to the world full stop. If these memoirs (underline memoirs) prove anything at all comma they prove . . . they prove . . . We have to think this out carefully, Tiggy.

Tiggy. See now, it's stopped. And it said rain continuing well into the afternoon. You can't depend on . . .

Lettice. I say WE HAVE TO THINK THIS OVER CAREFULLY, TIG-GEE. You keep on and on about the weather. Draw the curtains.

Tiggy. I don't like the curtains.

Lettice. What's wrong with them? They cost me a fortune.

Tiggy. *When* they were new. Oh, you should see some of the other flats in this block, so beautifully decorated. This wallpaper gives me the pip, Dame Lettice. Diamond-patterned — all over the flat, faded diamond-patterned. What colour was it when it was new?

Lettice. As I say, Tiggy, if you are not satisfied you can go elsewhere.

Tiggy. (*Reading from newspaper.*) 'Temperature slightly above average. Later fog——'
It's a pity the curtains look like the fog, Dame Lettice. They look like a drab velvet fog. So do the

walls, they are a diamond-patterned fog. You would think we were living in a cellar instead of a third-floor flat in the very best quarter. You have no colour sense, Dame Lettice, that's your trouble.

Lettice. Sombre shades, Tiggy, are conducive to the life of the imagination. Draw the curtains.

(*Curtains drawn*)

Tiggy. It puts me off my stroke, this room. Now, if you would only get your Regency chairs upholstered, say, in a nice striped brocade, and if you would only get rid of that smoky old paraffin stove . . . and if you would only tidy up all those old papers . . .

Lettice. Sh-sh-sh. Listen! Isn't that a key in the front door?

Tiggy. No. Couldn't be.

Lettice. I thought it might be Roy.

Tiggy. No. Couldn't be Roy.

Lettice. What do you mean, *couldn't* be Roy? I want the truth, Tiggy.

Tiggy. Afghanistan — principal exports: lambskin, fruit, cotton, wool, carpets, spices. . . .

Lettice. Has he gone to Afghanistan? Tiggy, if you know anything at all, you must tell me what you know.

Tiggy. A plus B squared equals A squared plus two AB plus B squared.

Lettice. Tiggy, you are amusing, Tiggy. Now, Tiggy, if you have the least clue as to my nephew's where-abouts . . . Tiggy, you know how I've been worrying about Roy . . . where do you think he can be?

Tiggy. Well, as I was saying yesterday, wherever he's gone, he's gone by air. I know he left from London Airport, as I told you yesterday.

Lettice. You said nothing of the sort yesterday. Tiggy, you are making this up.

Tiggy. No, no, Dame Lettice, I told you the day after he disappeared that he had left from London Airport. Don't you remember I said . . .

Lettice. You said nothing of the kind. I have been making enquiries all over England for the past three weeks. How do you know he left from London Airport?

Tiggy. I heard him at the street door giving directions to the taxi driver. Lebanon — gold, citrus, apples, wool, cotton, vegetables, hides and skins. . . .

Lettice. Roy must be abroad. Why didn't you tell me this before, Tiggy?

Tiggy. Oh I did, Dame Lettice. It's your memory again. Remember how bad your memory is. Remember . . .

Lettice. Where's that letter? Tiggy, find Roy's letter.

(*Looking amongst papers*)

Is it under the sofa, Tiggy?

Tiggy. No. Couldn't be.

Lettice. Tiggy, I wish you would do something about these papers lying all over the place. How can I find Roy's letters among all this muddle . . .? Papers, papers . . .

(*Papers turned over*)

Why don't you file them away, Tiggy?

Tiggy. The filing cabinets are full.

Lettice. We shall have to order more.

Tiggy. There's no room in the flat for more filing cabinets, is there now? Let's be honest. There are two in Roy's room, three in mine, that makes five. Four in here, three in . . . oh, and such dreary articles, practically the colour of mud. Do you know what they look like to me? — Those battered old jeeps that the Yanks used to go about in during the war. Ah, remember the Yanks, Dame Lettice! Those were the days. There was one called Lance; he was . . .

Lettice. (*Turning over papers.*) Tiggy, where is Roy's letter?

Tiggy. It's lost.

Lettice. What do you mean, it's lost?

Tiggy. But I know it by heart; it goes, 'Dear Auntie, I do not know how long I shall be away. Please do not attempt to locate me. Don't follow. I shall explain on my return. Yours, Roy.'

Lettice. Why should he go abroad at this time of year? Tiggy, if only he didn't have so many sides to his personality, one would know where one stood.

Tiggy. He may be in trouble. He may have gone into hiding, have you thought of that? Consulo, consulĕre, consului, consultum, verb to consult. Carpo, carpĕre, carpsi, carpsum, verb to pluck. Oh, Dame Lettice, do you remember that friend of Roy's by name of Trevor? No, you won't remember with your memory, Dame Lettice. That person he knows, called Trevor, remember, he was mixed up in the shooting case at St. John's Wood, remember, something to do with Sylvia Tree. Don't you remember Sylvia Tree, that dark girl? The case came up, remember, I think there were drugs mentioned.

Lettice. I do recall a Trevor. Roy brought him here one Sunday. There's nothing wrong with my memory, Tiggy.

Tiggy. Oh, yes, there is, Dame Lettice. It's the smoke from the stove. Paraffin fumes are so bad for the memory. You have forgotten that Roy was *very interested* in Trevor and Sylvia Tree. He wanted to save their souls.

Lettice. Tiggy, do you think Roy has got himself *mixed up in something*? He is due back at the Theological College in two days' time. He might have gone anywhere, he is so good at languages. Do you think he could be mixed up in . . .

Tiggy. Yes, I'm sure of it. Syria: population three point eight million, area seventy thousand eight hundred square miles; principal exports: cereals, animals, cotton, textiles, wool . . . He says in his letter he will explain on his return. I should forget about him in the meantime if I were you, Dame Lettice.

Lettice. Tiggy, you are dropping ash on the carpet, do be careful.

Tiggy. Oh, it will blend in. The father of Shem was Noah. Don Quixote is the hero of the book by that name written by the Spaniard Cervantes. I am going to win that twelve hundred on the General Knowledge Quiz, I feel it in my bones. Oh, how wonderful! I say, Dame Lettice, *he will explain on his return.*

Lettice. There is an ashtray in Roy's room; Tiggy, go and fetch it.

Tiggy. Oh-oh-oh. I don't like going in there. All those water colours, they remind me of poor Roy. Suppose something has happened to him? But never mind, Dame Lettice, he will explain on his return.

Lettice. What does he mean, he will explain on his return? I only hope his theological studies have not gone to his head.

Tiggy. I think they must have. I expect he has gone chasing Sylvia Tree.

Lettice. Who is Sylvia?

Tiggy. Friend of Trevor. Roy said she was a witch.

Lettice. Did he? What did he mean, a witch? Why should a theological student run after a witch?

Tiggy. To catch her, I suppose. And he will explain on his return. Hengist and Horsa were the reputed leaders of the first Anglo-Saxon invasion. . . .

(Fade)

Lettice. What can he mean, he will explain on his return? I shall keep him waiting, of course. And then I shall say to him, 'Oh, hallo, Roy, enjoy your trip?' And he will say to me, 'Enjoy it! If only you knew . . .'

Roy. If only you knew the difficulties I have been facing. Do you remember Sylvia Tree?

Lettice. Of course. A dark girl, a friend of Trevor what's-his-name.

Tiggy. *(From distance.)* Don't start imagining things, Dame Lettice. You know it doesn't do any good.

Lettice. A dark girl, a friend of Trevor what's-his-name.

Roy. A very dark girl. She's a witch. Do you know what I've discovered? I discovered a complete witchcraft organisation in St. John's Wood. You think witch-craft does not exist, don't you? Well, you're wrong.

Lettice. Roy, what are you talking about? Your theo-logical studies . . .

Roy. I had suspicions three months ago. I began to take notes. I will read them to you. One, Sylvia Tree is the leader and Trevor Loam is her accomplice. Two, they hold a Sabbath once a month where they drink human blood. Three, they bewitch men and motor cars. Four, they make wax images of their enemies and stick pins into them. Five, they have made a covenant with the Devil. Six, they . . .

Lettice. How much did you spend on this trip abroad?

Roy. Use your imagination, Auntie. (*Starts coughing.*) Oh, that dreadful paraffin stove!

Lettice. How much?

Roy. Would you grudge a few pounds for the cause of God and justice? Sylvia Tree found out that I was watching her. She went abroad. I followed her, of course. I found her in Stuttgart drinking coffee.

Lettice. Sit down, Roy, and let us get this straight. No, don't sit on that Regency chair. I won't have people sitting on my good chairs. Sit on the sofa and mind the papers. I don't see why you should have followed this Sylvia Tree. You ought to have informed the police and left it to them.

Roy. The police are far too superstitious. They won't touch witchcraft. And do you realise it is my duty to the cloth to rout the Devil personally. There are many known methods of discovering a witch. They are quite reliable methods. You can subject them to physical

examination and to interrogation. A witch may have
supernumerary teats, she may fail to respond to prick-
ings. Sylvia, for instance, has an area of her body
which is insensate to the prick of a pin. I have proved
it. I have proved . . .

Lettice. You haven't been sticking pins into a girl?

Roy. Indeed yes. What else could I do? I captured
Sylvia and applied all the known tests. . . . Is that
someone at the door?

Lettice. No, I don't hear anyone at the door. Tell
me . . .

Roy. Oh, I thought it might be the police. Unfortu-
nately, you see, Trevor found me putting Sylvia to the
test, and of course, being her accomplice, he is very
cross. I escaped. But he has been to the police. You
must hide me somewhere, Auntie, until the fuss dies
down. Then I shall emerge, and theology will take its
course, and we shall triumph over . . .

(*Fade*)

Lettice. Tiggy, where are you? Tiggy — where's that
girl? Tiggy! Tiggy!

(*Fade*)
(*Scene pause*)

Tiggy. Hallo, Dame Lettice, how are we?

Lettice. Tiggy, where have you been?

Tiggy. Oh, I went out for half an hour to give myself a
change.

Lettice. I do wish you had told me beforehand, Tiggy.
And it's so foggy outside. I think there must be something wrong with you, Tiggy, to go out in . . .

Tiggy. It's foggy inside.

Lettice. Oh, Tiggy, it's unbearable. I . . .

Tiggy. I'm glad you see that, Dame Lettice. I'm glad you are beginning to see my point of view. . . .

Lettice. I mean, about Roy. To think of Roy, Tiggy! I think he has gone off his head.

Tiggy. Not him.

Lettice. Now suppose, Tiggy, he has gone to hunt this witch. And suppose . . .

Tiggy. What witch?

Lettice. Sylvia Tree. You told me yourself, Tiggy, he thinks she is a witch.

Tiggy. Not me. I never mentioned witch. You have such an imagination, Dame Lettice. And *no* memory. Known throughout the world as 'The Whispering Giant', the Bristol Britannia is the largest turbo-prop airliner in service today. The Britannia 310, powered by four Bristol Proteus . . .

Lettice. Shut up, Tiggy. Just you shut up. We are wasting our time. Where had we got to? Read the whole sentence.

Tiggy. You didn't finish the sentence.

(*Curtain drawn back*)

See, look, it's foggy outside. Almost as bad as inside.

Lettice. Read the previous sentence, Tiggy. Hurry up.

(*Pause while Tiggy finds the place*)

Tiggy. 'It has therefore always been difficult for me, with so many sides to my personality, to present only one of those sides to the world. If these memoirs prove anything at all, they prove . . .'

Lettice. They prove ... they prove ... the supremacy of the world of ... of ...

Tiggy. Imagination. I do think it a pity to spoil the interior of a luxury flat like this with all the murky stuff you've put into it. ...

Lettice. (*Shouting her down.*) The supremacy of the world of imagination comma a world in which literally anything can happen comma over the mundane facts of ... of ...

Tiggy. Everyday life.

Lettice. Everyday life. Listen! ... There's the key in the door.

Tiggy. No. Couldn't be.

Lettice. I thought it might be Roy.

Tiggy. Couldn't be.

Lettice. Couldn't it? Oh, couldn't it? You seem to know a lot. You seem to forget Roy is a student of theology, and therefore has some sense of responsibility towards his only relative.

Tiggy. You never know how theology's going to take a young man. Roy has got ideas about religion, he has got his own ideas, I can tell you that much.

Lettice. Tiggy, I have thought over the question whether he has gone to hunt witches. I do not really believe, Tiggy, that Roy, who is so good at languages, would go abroad and waste them on a witch.

Tiggy. Captain Hornblower is the central character in C. S. Forester's series of books. Theology's a dangerous subject for a sensitive young man like Roy with funny ideas.

Lettice. Roy is perfectly orthodox. The Principal of the Theological College wrote to me . . .

Tiggy. Did you notice when he came home he wouldn't eat meat on a Friday? Fish on a Friday keep your nose tidy.

Lettice. Oh, that is quite common among theological students, Tiggy. . . .

Tiggy. Did you see him reading from a Roman breviary? It was all in Latin. I saw it. Lord Palmerston was British Prime Minister from 1855 to 1858.

Lettice. Tiggy, you must either practise for the Quiz in your spare time or leave. The distractions are . . .

Tiggy. If I win I'll leave. Just imagine Roy flitting round the back streets of the Vatican. You shouldn't have put him in for Holy Orders, Dame Lettice. I told you at the time.

Lettice. What do you mean, the Vatican?

Tiggy. Gliding through the dark alleys, in and out the archways, murmuring with Jesuits. Up the winding staircase . . . breathing incense. And he's so good at languages, how they would love to catch him!

Lettice. Oh, I shouldn't stand for it, I should never stand for it. Not another penny would he get from me, Tiggy. Can you imagine such a thing?

Tiggy. Quite clearly. That's what he means when he says, 'I will explain on my return.'

Lettice. I shall keep calm, Tiggy. I shall say to him, 'Oh, hallo, Roy, enjoyed your trip?' and he'll say, 'Well, *enjoyed* is hardly . . .'

(*Fade*)

Roy. . . . *enjoyed* is hardly the word. However, I can accurately say that my journey and mission were satisfactory.

Lettice. You flew home, I suppose?

Roy. No, hitch-hiked. Fasting. Like a pilgrim.

Lettice. I thought you probably came on wings.

Roy. Oh, no. I have changed my religion, Auntie, since I came on vacation. Remember the first day, it was raining? Well, it was *such* a wet day that I *simply* decided to go over to Rome.

Lettice. Roy, have you forgotten what Dr. Keble said to your great-great-grandfather?

Roy. Yes, absolutely.

Lettice. Not another penny of mine do you get, Roy. I hope you understand that, Roy.

Roy. Yes, absolutely. It doesn't make the slightest difference. I have completely renounced the world, my past errors, you and Tiggy. I have come to say good-bye. (*Starts coughing.*) Oh dear, my chest! your stove! (*Gasping.*) I return to Rome tonight. Two years at Rome. Then to the mission field. . . . (*Fading out.*) Fortunately I am good at languages . . . Perpetual vows . . . The Congo . . . Behind the Iron Curtain. . . .

Lettice. Are you there, Tiggy? Tiggy, where are you? Tiggy! It is most unpleasant never knowing where you are . . . Tiggy!

(*Fading out*)

I have something important . . .

(*Scene pause*)

Lettice. Tiggy, where have you been?

Tiggy. Oh, I was just having a lay-down.

Lettice. *Lie*-down.

Tiggy. A lie-down. You been day-dreaming again?

Lettice. No, Tiggy, just thinking.

Tiggy. Well, it's very bad for you. What have you been thinking about?

Lettice. Just let me get my breath, Tiggy. My head aches.

Tiggy. Poor Roy. Do you know, I'm really sorry for Roy.

Lettice. Oh, Tiggy, can't we save him? He has gone over to Rome.

Tiggy. Not him.

Lettice. I know it in my bones.

Tiggy. Your bones are in error. Do you believe in witchcraft, Dame Lettice?

Lettice. Don't be absurd, Tiggy. This is serious. Poor Roy! The Vatican . . . the winding alleyways . . . perpetual vows. After all my efforts . . .

Tiggy. Would you say, just speaking impersonally, Dame Lettice, that one can affect the course of nature by the power of thought?

Lettice. Tiggy, I am not interested in your Quiz at this moment.

Tiggy. I just wanted to know, Dame Lettice, if you did believe in witchcraft. Because I do. Do you know what I think?

Lettice. I must send a telegram to the Theological College right away. They must get in touch with Roy at Rome. Tiggy, take down this wire. Are you ready? Address to the Principal . . .

Tiggy. Do you know what I think? I think you practise witchcraft on poor Roy. You are always making a wax image of him and sticking pins into it.

Lettice. Stop your nonsense, Tiggy, and take this wire. 'The Principal, the Theological College . . .'

Tiggy. A wax image and sticking pins into it. There's no point in sending a wire. Poor Roy hasn't changed his religion. That I do know.

Lettice. How do you know? The truth, Tiggy.

Tiggy. He never had a religion in the first place.

Lettice. Well, Tiggy, you yourself suggested . . .

Tiggy. It's your imagination again, Dame Lettice. The way you keep working over poor Roy in your mind, it's like sticking pins into his image. Poor Roy, I *am* sorry for him. 'Glorious First of June' commemorates the British naval victory off Ushant, 1794. Charles XII of Sweden, 1682 to 1718, was a courageous but frequently impulsive monarch. Benvenuto Cellini . . .

Lettice. I pay you a wage. You do admit that, Tiggy, don't you?

Tiggy. I know what you're going to say next. 'I have made *my* house *your* home, Tig-gee.' I know how you talk; you see, I know how you talk.

Lettice. Where had we got to? I want the last sentence, that's all I'm asking. It's a small thing . . .

Tiggy. 'If these memoirs prove anything at all, they prove the supremacy of the world of imagination, a world in which literally anything can happen, over the mundane facts of everyday life.'

Lettice. Full stop, new paragraph. It has always been my rule to submit all personal problems to the test of the imagination full stop. When I first entered politics in 1920 — Tiggy, where's my diary for 1920?

Tiggy. Everyone knows what you said to Lloyd George in 1920. You've quoted it dozens of times.

Lettice. Tiggy, I repeat. Where's my diary for 1920?

Tiggy. You said to Lloyd George, 'Politics, my dear Lloyd George, are imagination and imagination is politics.'

Lettice. (*Turning over papers.*) Where's that diary?

Tiggy. And he replied, 'You are very self-observant, Madam.'

Lettice. Oh no, he didn't. Oh no, Tiggy, he did not. There are some things, Tiggy, let me tell you, which are a closed book to you. Where's the diary for 1920. . . .

(*Papers turned over*)

1921 . . . '29 . . . 1936 . . . that's not it. Where . . .

Tiggy. Sh-sh-sh. What's that noise?

Lettice. Where? Could it be . . .?

Tiggy. No. Couldn't be. The Julian calendar is the calendar instituted by Julius Caesar in 46 b.c. The Venus's Fly-Trap is an insect-devouring plant. He may be dabbling in politics, have you thought of that?

Lettice. Roy has no brain for politics, Tiggy, even though he is good at languages. You need imagination for politics. If he'd shown any promise for politics, I should never have put him in for theology.

Tiggy. Ah — your memory's going. You don't recall his friend Trevor from St. John's Wood. You don't remember Sylvia Tree.

Lettice. Certainly I do. They are connected with witchcraft. I hardly think Roy is interested in witchcraft in this weather.

Tiggy. Oh, it's really sad the way you wander off the subject, Dame Lettice. I blame the wallpaper, it's bound to have an effect. I was only saying about their politics, but if you don't want to hear . . .

Lettice. Is there anything *shady* about them, Tiggy?

Tiggy. Well, they are members of the Party, I know it for a fact. The Sea Cucumber is a member of the starfish family. The Leaning Tower of Soo Chow, China, is over one thousand three hundred years old. . .

(*Fade*)

(*Sound of key in door and rapid footsteps. Door bangs. Roy breathless.*)

Roy. A little job abroad. I can't go into details, Auntie, you must realise that. It was just a little job. . . . Well, I'll tell you one thing, but you must treat it as confidential. I've been in Yugoslavia doing a little job there. Has anybody been here asking for me?

Lettice. Sit down, Roy. Have you enjoyed your trip?

Roy. Has anyone been looking for me? Anybody asking questions?

Lettice. No, Roy, not a soul.

Roy. Switch out the light while I look out of the window.

(*Goes to window*)

I thought so! There are shadows lurking in the fog. The flat is being watched. Auntie, you must hide me. Where can I go?

Lettice. This is all very shady, Roy. Kindly draw those curtains and switch on the light.

(*Curtains drawn*)

Roy. If anyone rings the door bell, don't answer it. If the telephone rings, don't answer. (*Coughs.*) Please turn off that ghastly stove. I must find a hiding-place. The linen cupboard is too obvious. Your wardrobe . . . oh, they always look in wardrobes. What about the cupboard in Tiggy's bedroom? There are lots of old boxes there, I might look like one of them.

Lettice. From whom are you hiding?

Roy. M.I.5. They've got Sylvia already. Trevor got away. He took to the mountains.

Lettice. What were you doing in Yugoslavia, Roy?

Roy. A little job for the Party. A *nice* little job. You may see something in the papers tomorrow.

Lettice. Not about you, Roy?

Roy. No. About Yugoslavia. I must go and prepare a place in Tiggy's cupboard. They might be coming for me any time.

Lettice. You realise, Roy, not another penny do you get out of me while you remain a Communist.

Roy. Money? Dear me, don't let that bother you. I've made a packet. All that worries me is . . .

Lettice. I suppose you did not stop to think of my reputation. . . .

Roy. And what were you doing in 1932?

Lettice. Now, Roy, you know I gave up the Fascist movement as soon as . . .

Roy. As soon as you thought it would ruin your reputation. Our cause is above reputation. We are not finished, we are only beginning. We shall . . .

Lettice. To think what Bonar Law said to your father in 1922! He said . . .

Roy. Listen! There's someone outside the door. Put out all the lights. I'm going to hide. Where's Tiggy? Tiggy will conceal me. Tiggy!

(*Door bell*)

Tiggy! Tiggy!

Lettice. Tiggy, where are you? Tiggy!

(*Fade*)
(*Scene pause*)

Lettice. Tiggy, this is not good enough. I have been calling you, I . . .

Tiggy. (*Approaching.*) What's the matter? I don't get any time to myself on this job. That's the worst of living in. I have been tidying up the cupboard in my room. What do you want?

Lettice. Tiggy, I feel ill.

Tiggy. You must have eaten something.

Lettice. I haven't eaten anything.

Tiggy. You've been drinking something.

Lettice. Tiggy, you know I don't take drink. My blood pressure . . .

Tiggy. You've been drinking Roy's life blood, you old succubus.

Lettice. I have been meditating.

Tiggy. Meditating is eating in the spiritual sense. I should take up smoking if I were you, Dame Lettice, it's good for the nerves.

Lettice. Oh, Tiggy, I read an article about smoking, it's so dangerous.

Tiggy. Hell is more dangerous. You should chew gum, Dame Lettice. That helps to keep the mind under control and provides a soothing action for the jaws.

Lettice. If Roy has become a Communist, Tiggy, I think I shall go mad.

Tiggy. Well, you won't have to go far. No, don't cry, Dame Lettice. I can't bear to see you cry. Life is too short, Dame Lettice, for tears. Lima is the capital of Peru. The capital of Yemen is Sana. If you don't want me just now I think I'll go and finish cleaning out the cupboard. It ought to be done before Roy comes back.

Lettice. What has Roy to do with the cupboard in your bedroom? Tiggy, he is coming here to hide, isn't he? . . . Don't go, Tiggy.

Tiggy. He usually hides in the cupboard in my bedroom. He waits till my day's work is finished and then he tells me all his little troubles.

Lettice. I hope he doesn't notice your teeth. Tiggy, you have worse teeth than any woman I know. What troubles can Roy have to tell you, I ask you, Tiggy, how can he have any troubles? The Theological College is quiet, secluded and conducive to the untroubled mind. He has a generous allowance from me, and one day will inherit all I possess — that's when I'm gone, Tiggy, when I'm gone. But he had better give a good account of himself on his return or not another penny does he get from me. My mind is made up.

Tiggy. Suppose he gets married?

Lettice. Roy is a born celibate, Tiggy, how could he get married, I ask you, can you see Roy getting married?

Tiggy. If you stretch your imagination a little, perhaps . . .

Lettice. *My* imagination! There's nothing wrong with my imagination. You stretch yours, Tiggy, and see if you can imagine Roy getting married to a girl. He doesn't know any girls.

Tiggy. There's Sylvia Tree.

Lettice. Is she after him? I say, Tiggy, between old friends, what has Roy confided to you about Sylvia Tree?

(*Door bell*)

Tiggy. There's the door bell.

Lettice. It may be Roy. He may have lost his key.

Tiggy. No. Couldn't be Roy. It's too early.

(*Door bell*)

Lettice. Quickly, Tiggy, go and see who it is.

Tiggy. It's a telegram——

(*Opens it*)

'Home tonight. Love, Roy.'

Lettice. Give it to me. Let me see it.

Tiggy. It's mine, it's addressed to me.

Lettice. That must be a mistake. Let me see the telegram. Where did he send it from?

Tiggy. Brest. As I expected.

Lettice. In Russia, I knew it!

Tiggy. No, Brest in Brittany. Doesn't that ring a bell, Dame Lettice?

Lettice. A ring at the bell? It may be Roy.

Tiggy. No, couldn't be. He's in *Brittany* — you know, don't you, that there's a Druid movement in Brittany?

Look at the fog, how thick it is. I hope Roy won't be caught in it. Funny to think of Roy as a Druid.

Lettice. My dear Tiggy, Roy hasn't time to be a Druid.

Tiggy. Brest is also a famous hideout for international smuggling gangs, you know that, don't you? I am just telling you the facts.

Lettice. You will never convince me Roy has the wits for smuggling.

Tiggy. Only the day before he left he said to me — as he came out of my cupboard — he said, 'Independence of thought, Tiggy, and financial independence as well. Those are what I need.' Independence Day in Ceylon is 4th February. Independence Day in the U.S.A. is 4th July.

(*Fade*)

Roy. But you don't know anything *about* the Druid movement, Auntie. It's a deep subject. Since I was initiated three months ago life has been far more meaningful. (*Coughs slightly.*) I have seen the sun rise at Stonehenge. (*Coughs.*) I have assisted at the rites on Tower Hill, the Isle of Mull, and at Avebury, and I have just been to Brittany to participate in a rite of the utmost antiquity — it was most stimulating. If you knew anything of the elaborate symbolism of nature worship, Auntie, you would . . . (*Coughs.*) Oh, that nasty stove . . . after the pure air of Brittany! . . .

Lettice. Not another penny do you get from me, Roy. I won't countenance a crank in the family.

Roy. (*His voice becomes remote and hollow, and he speaks in a sort of chant.*) Inde-pendence of thought. The Theological College was quite un-bearable. It was driving

188

me to dis-traction till I dis-covered Inde-pendence.
Spirit-ual Inde-pendence.

Tiggy. (*Her voice has the same quality as Roy's above.*)
Inde-pendence Day, Colombia, 20th July. Inde-
pendence Day, Belgium, 21st July. Syl-via Tree has
inde-pendent means.

Lettice. Oh, by the way, Roy, is Sylvia Tree a Druid?

Roy. (*Normal voice.*) Not yet. But she has agreed to
symbolise the Fruits of the Earth at our next ceremony.
You see, the Fruits of the Earth has to be a non-Druid.
But Sylvia will become a Druid one day, like me. She
has independent means.

Lettice. I should never have thought, Roy, that you
would stoop to marrying a woman for her money. I
would rather see you going in for the Quiz like Tiggy.
Besides, are you sure Miss Tree will accept you? If she
has independent means, surely . . .

Roy. (*Character changes to tough.*) Me marry Sylvia
Tree? I'm out for big money, my dear. Sylvia has
only a pittance. Turn off that stove.

Lettice. You won't make money by being a Druid, Roy.
Have some sense, you are just like your father.

Tiggy. (*Distant.*) Tell her why you have been to
Brittany, Roy.

Lettice. (*Voice raised.*) You keep out of this, Tiggy. Roy
has been to Brittany to meet the Druids.

Roy. No, Auntie. I've been to meet J.A.17 and F.10
and Q.L.215. These are my contacts. We had a little
job to do, you see. Now you've got to hide me somewhere because they're after me, see?

Lettice. A little job for the Party! I knew it. What are you doing, Roy? — Leave that stove alone. Don't you touch it.

Roy. Getcher.

Lettice. A little job for the Party! (*Coughs.*) Oh, I am overcome. Light that stove again immediately. A little job for the . . .!

Roy. Not for the Party, dear. For number one. A few carton cases packed with bank notes and other items have been delivered by sea to Mr. J.A.17, Mr. F.10, and Mr. Q.L.215. It was a rough passage; I don't care for these little fishing boats. But it was worth it — or will be, Auntie dear, if you can hide me somewhere. M.I.5 have got poor old Q.L.215, and I don't know how much he's told them. Where can I hide if necessary? Think of something, you old gin-trap.

Lettice. Tiggy, where are you?

Roy. Of course . . . Tiggy will help. There's a deep cupboard in her bedroom, I'll get in there and she can pull the wardrobe in front of the door. Now remember . . .

Lettice. Tiggy! I want you.

Tiggy. (*Approaching from a distance*) . . . and his most famous saying was 'Live! Our servants can do it for us.' I never get a minute to myself. I am tidying up the cupboard in my potty little bedroom. Roy likes hiding in there. You've been *at* poor Roy again, haven't you? Sticking pins . . .

Lettice. He inherits nothing, do you understand, Tiggy. Not a penny if he has taken up smuggling.

Tiggy. I thought it was Druids. One minute you talk about Druids and the next minute you talk about smuggling. I suggest you keep to one subject. The Treaty of Locarno, 1925.

(*Curtains drawn back*)

Look at the fog out there, how thick it is. Almost as bad as the smoke from . . .

Lettice. There's nothing wrong with my stove. Draw those curtains, Tiggy, and stop wasting time. Smuggling was the last idea I had. It just came to me. I feel terrible. What time do you think he will arrive?

Tiggy. Any time tonight.

Lettice. I wonder if he will come by air or fishing boat?

Tiggy. By air. First-class passage paid.

Lettice. You seem to know a lot.

Tiggy. Poor Roy.

Lettice. It isn't, Tiggy, as if I had ever refused him his independence. I've always allowed him to do anything he likes. I just want to know *what* he's doing. So I don't see why you should say 'poor Roy' like that.

Tiggy. Poor Roy, suppose he's dead. Suppose his plane has crashed in the fog and he's lying dead at this very moment.

Lettice. What a ghastly thought. Ring the airport at once, Tiggy.

Tiggy. Killed by the power of your wicked imagination.

Lettice. Ring the airport, Tiggy, and enquire.

Tiggy. Which airport? How do we know what airport he left from or what plane he took? Anyway, if he's dead, he's dead, and he and I shall never be married. You always did say he was a born celibate.

Lettice. What are you saying — *married*?

Tiggy. Roy and I are engaged to be married. Limnology is the division of biology dealing with fresh-water organisms.

Lettice. That I don't believe.

Tiggy. Perfectly true. We are engaged to be married and limnology is . . .

Lettice. We are wasting precious time, Tiggy. I can't bear waste of time. Sit down, Tiggy. Now, my memoirs. Where did we get to? Read the last paragraph. You are fifteen years older than Roy. A *good* fifteen years. And your teeth — really, Tiggy. The last paragraph, if you please.

Tiggy. 'It has always been my rule to submit all personal problems to the test of the imagination full stop. When I first entered politics in 1920 . . .'

Lettice. My diary for 1920. Haven't you found it yet? Look here, Tiggy, there is something we must get clear. If you are thinking of running after Roy at your time of life, I must tell you there is no chance for you. Roy is not the marrying type, and if he were, there would be no chance for you. Just use your imagination. I feel, of course, that I shall have to warn poor Roy of this quite absurd notion you have in your head. He is very sensitive and might easily be led into something foolish.

Tiggy. Sh-sh-sh. There's the key in the front door.

(*Key opening front door. Door closes. Footsteps*)
It *is* Roy. It really is. He's early.

Lettice. At last! Are you sure, Tiggy?

Tiggy. Of course I'm sure. (*Footsteps stop.*) Roy!

(*Opens door of room*)

Roy! Where are you? Oh, he's hiding somewhere. Roy, we heard you. Come out.

Roy. Here I am.

Tiggy. Oh, you gave me a fright! Where were you hiding?

Lettice. Hallo, Roy, had a nice trip? Come and sit down. That will be all for now, Tiggy.

Tiggy. Good.

Lettice. I said that will be all for now, Tig-gee.

Tiggy. Good. Well, I'll just relax and talk to Roy. We've been worried about you, Roy, coming through this fog. I quite expected your plane to be cancelled. You don't look too well, are you all right?

Lettice. Ring down and ask them to send up the menu, Tiggy.

Roy. I had something to eat on the plane, thanks.

Lettice. Pour yourself a drink, Roy. You don't look very well. Are you all right?

Roy. I feel a little frail, Auntie.

Lettice. Poor boy. What will you drink?

Roy. Nothing, thanks.

Tiggy. It's the effect of the paraffin fumes. Roy has not got a strong stomach, Dame Lettice, at the best of times.

Lettice. I don't mind the stove. Not a bit.

Tiggy. I say, Roy, did you get it fixed up? You know what I mean.

Roy. Oh, yes, most successfully.

Tiggy. Hooray! He's got the job.

Lettice. What job?

Roy. A job with a tourist agency. They were most impressed by my knowledge of languages.

Lettice. Whatever has come over you, Roy? There is no need for you to take a job with a tourist agency.

Roy. I wanted to be independent and get married to Tiggy, that's all.

Tiggy. There, you see, Dame Lettice, what did I tell you?

Lettice. Marry Tiggy! But Tiggy is . . . her teeth . . .

Tiggy. Just a moment, just a moment, Dame Lettice. It will be a much healthier life for Roy, taking tourists round Europe in the summer months and returning to a faithful and capable wife in the winter. You know I'm capable, Dame Lettice. You know . . .

Lettice. Not another penny of mine do you get, Roy.

Roy. I don't need another penny.

Tiggy. And if I win the Quiz — oh, if I win the Quiz — won't we have a party!

Lettice. Sit down and compose yourself, Tiggy. Roy, you look dreadfully pale. Are you all right? Let me feel your pulse.

Roy. No. Don't touch me.

Tiggy. Poor Roy! Let *me* feel your . . .

Roy. Stand back. Don't touch me.

Lettice. Oh, something has happened to Roy.

Tiggy. Roy! Oh, Roy, I can see through you.

Lettice. I hope he can see through *you*, Tiggy.

Tiggy. I can see right through him and out at the other side. Look! There's the back of the sofa and the wall behind him. He looks like a ghost. See, Dame Lettice, he's transparent.

Lettice. Stand up, Roy. There's something the matter with you.

Tiggy. Turn round, Roy. Let me have a look . . . this murky room . . .

Lettice. Come over here, Roy, under the light. . . .

Tiggy. Take no notice of her, Roy. Just stand still a minute and let me see . . .

Lettice. Tiggy, don't interfere. Over here, Roy, till I look at . . . oh, Tiggy, oh, he's quite insubstantial, like the fog. Whatever is the matter with you, Roy?

Roy. (*Voice rather hollow and 'sinister' from this point.*) The plane did crash, Tiggy. Ten minutes ago. I was killed in the crash.

Lettice. Oh, Roy, you are not a ghost, are you?

Roy. Well, yes, Auntie, as a matter of fact, yes, I am. But it won't make much difference, will it? I mean to say . . .

Lettice. I am going to faint.

Roy. So is Tiggy. Tiggy's going to faint, a knowledgeable girl like Tiggy! Oh, I wish you wouldn't both faint. I mean to say, what are you going to do when you come round again? And after all, I shall be coming back again, quite often . . . Any time you like . . . Any time. . . .

A Member of the Family

'You must,' said Richard, suddenly, one day in November, 'come and meet my mother.'

Trudy, who had been waiting a long time for this invitation, after all was amazed.

'I should like you,' said Richard, 'to meet my mother. She's looking forward to it.'

'Oh, does she know about me?'

'Rather,' Richard said.

'Oh!'

'No need to be nervous,' Richard said. 'She's awfully sweet.'

'Oh, I'm sure she is. Yes, of course, I'd love——'

'Come to tea on Sunday,' he said.

They had met the previous June in a lake town in Southern Austria. Trudy had gone with a young woman who had a bed-sitting-room in Kensington just below Trudy's room. This young woman could speak German, whereas Trudy couldn't.

Bleilach was one of the cheaper lake towns; in fact, cheaper was a way of putting it: it was cheap.

'Gwen, I didn't realise it ever rained here,' Trudy said on their third day. 'It's all rather like Wales,' she said, standing by the closed double windows of their room regarding the downpour and imagining the mountains which indeed were there, but invisible.

'You said that yesterday,' Gwen said, 'and it was quite fine yesterday. Yesterday you said it was like Wales.'

'Well, it rained a bit yesterday.'

'But the sun was shining when you said it was like Wales.'

'Well, so it is.'

'On a much larger scale, I should say,' Gwen said.

'I didn't realise it would be so wet.' Then Trudy could almost hear Gwen counting twenty.

'You have to take your chance,' Gwen said. 'This is an unfortunate summer.'

The pelting of the rain increased as if in confirmation.

Trudy thought, I'd better shut up. But suicidally: 'Wouldn't it be better if we moved to a slightly more expensive place?' she said.

'The rain falls on the expensive places too. It falls on the just and the unjust alike.'

Gwen was thirty-five, a schoolteacher. She wore her hair and her clothes and her bit of lipstick in such a way that, standing by the window looking out at the rain, it occurred to Trudy like a revelation that Gwen had given up all thoughts of marriage. 'On the just and the unjust alike,' said Gwen, turning her maddening imperturbable eyes upon Trudy, as if to say, you are the unjust and I'm the just.

Next day was fine. They swam in the lake. They sat drinking apple juice under the red and yellow awnings on the terrace of their guest-house and gazed at the innocent smiling mountain. They paraded —

Gwen in her navy-blue shorts and Trudy in her puffy sun-suit — along the lake-side where marched also the lean brown camping youths from all over the globe, the fat print-frocked mothers and double-chinned fathers from Germany followed by their blonde sedate young, and the English women with their perms.

'There aren't any men about,' Trudy said.

'There are hundreds of men,' Gwen said, in a voice which meant, whatever do you mean?

'I really must try out my phrase-book,' Trudy said, for she had the feeling that if she were independent of Gwen as interpreter she might, as she expressed it to herself, have more of a chance.

'You might have more chance of meeting someone interesting that way,' Gwen said, for their close confinement by the rain had seemed to make her psychic, and she was continually putting Trudy's thoughts into words.

'Oh, I'm not here for that. I only wanted a rest, as I told you. I'm not——'

'Goodness, Richard!'

Gwen was actually speaking English to a man who was not apparently accompanied by a wife or aunt or sister.

He kissed Gwen on the cheek. She laughed and so did he. 'Well, well,' he said. He was not much taller than Gwen. He had dark crinkly hair and a small moustache of a light brown. He wore bathing trunks and his large chest was impressively bronze. 'What brings you here?' he said to Gwen, looking meanwhile at Trudy.

He was staying at an hotel on the other side of the lake. Each day for the rest of the fortnight he rowed over to meet them at ten in the morning, sometimes spending the whole day with them. Trudy was charmed, she could hardly believe in Gwen's friendly indifference to him, notwithstanding he was a teacher at the same grammar school as Gwen, who therefore saw him every day.

Every time he met them he kissed Gwen on the cheek.

'You seem to be on very good terms with him,' Trudy said.

'Oh, Richard's an old friend. I've known him for years.'

The second week, Gwen went off on various expeditions of her own and left them together.

'This is quite a connoisseur's place,' Richard informed Trudy, and he pointed out why, and in what choice way, it was so, and Trudy, charmed, saw in the peeling pastel stucco of the little town, the unnecessary floral balconies, the bulbous Slovene spires, something special after all. She felt she saw, through his eyes, a precious rightness in the women with their grey skirts and well-filled blouses who trod beside their husbands and their clean children.

'Are they all Austrians?' Trudy asked.

'No, some of them are German and French. But this place attracts the same type.'

Richard's eyes rested with appreciation on the young noisy campers whose tents were pitched in the lake-side field. The campers were long-limbed and animal, brightly and briefly dressed. They romped like galvanized goats, yet looked surprisingly virtuous.

'What are they saying to each other?' she enquired of Richard when a group of them passed by, shouting some words and laughing at each other through glistening red lips and very white teeth.

'They are talking about their fast M.G. racing cars.'

'Oh, have they got racing cars?'

'No, the racing cars they are talking about don't exist. Sometimes they talk about their film contracts which don't exist. That's why they laugh.'

'Not much of a sense of humour, have they?'

'They are of mixed nationalities, so they have to limit their humour to jokes which everyone can understand, and so they talk about racing cars which aren't there.'

Trudy giggled a little, to show willing. Richard told her he was thirty-five, which she thought feasible. She volunteered that she was not quite twenty-two. Whereupon Richard looked at her and looked away, and looked again and took her hand. For, as he told Gwen afterwards, this remarkable statement was almost an invitation to a love affair.

Their love affair began that afternoon, in a boat on the lake, when, barefoot, they had a game of placing sole to sole, heel to heel. Trudy squealed, and leaned back hard, pressing her feet against Richard's.

She squealed at Gwen when they met in their room later on. 'I'm having a heavenly time with Richard. I do so much like an older man.'

Gwen sat on her bed and gave Trudy a look of wonder. Then she said, 'He's not much older than you.'

'I've knocked a bit off my age,' Trudy said. 'Do you mind not letting on?'

'How much have you knocked off?'

'Seven years.'

'Very courageous,' Gwen said.

'What do you mean?'

'That you are brave.'

'Don't you think you're being a bit nasty?'

'No. It takes courage to start again and again. That's all I mean. Some women would find it boring.'

'Oh, I'm not an experienced girl at all,' Trudy said. 'Whatever made you think I was experienced?'

'It's true,' Gwen said, 'you show no signs of having profited by experience. Have you ever found it a successful tactic to remain twenty-two?'

'I believe you're jealous,' Trudy said. 'One expects this sort of thing from most older women, but somehow I didn't expect it from you.'

'One is always learning,' Gwen said.

Trudy fingered her curls. 'Yes, I have got a lot to learn from life,' she said, looking out of the window.

'God,' said Gwen, 'you haven't begun to believe that you're still twenty-two, have you?'

'Not quite twenty-two is how I put it to Richard,' Trudy said, 'and yes, I do feel it. That's my point. I don't feel a day older.'

The last day of their holidays Richard took Trudy rowing on the lake which reflected a grey low sky.

'It looks like Windermere today, doesn't it?' he said.

Trudy had not seen Windermere, but she said, yes it did, and gazed at him with shining twenty-two-year-old eyes.

'Sometimes this place,' he said, 'is very like Yorkshire, but only when the weather's bad. Or, over on the mountain side, Wales.'

'Exactly what I told Gwen,' Trudy said. 'I said Wales, I said, it's like Wales.'

'Well, of course, there's quite a difference, really. It——'

'But Gwen simply squashed the idea. You see, she's an older woman, and being a schoolmistress — it's so much different when a man's a teacher — being a woman teacher, she feels she can treat me like a kid. I suppose I must expect it.'

'Oh well——'

'How long have you known Gwen?'

'Several years,' he said. 'Gwen's all right, darling. A great friend of my mother, is Gwen. Quite a member of the family.'

Trudy wanted to move her lodgings in London but she was prevented from doing so by a desire to be near Gwen, who saw Richard daily at school, and who knew his mother so well. And therefore Gwen's experience of Richard filled in the gaps in his life which were unknown to Trudy and which intrigued her.

She would fling herself into Gwen's room. 'Gwen, what d'you think? There he was waiting outside the office and he drove me home, and he's calling for me at seven, and next week-end . . .'

Gwen frequently replied, 'You are out of breath. Have you got heart trouble?' — for Gwen's room was only on the first floor. And Trudy was furious with Gwen on these occasions for seeming not to understand that the breathlessness was all part of her only being twenty-two, and excited by the boy-friend.

'I think Richard's so exciting,' Trudy said. 'It's difficult to believe I've only known him a month.'

'Has he invited you home to meet his mother?' Gwen enquired.

'No — not yet. Oh, do you think he will?'

'Yes, I think so. One day I'm sure he will.'

'Oh, do you mean it?' Trudy flung her arms girlishly round Gwen's impassive neck.

'When is your father coming up?' Gwen said.

'Not for ages, if at all. He can't leave Leicester just now, and he hates London.'

'You must get him to come and ask Richard what his intentions are. A young girl like you needs protection.'

'Gwen, don't be silly.'

Often Trudy would question Gwen about Richard and his mother.

'Are they well off? Is she a well-bred woman? What's the house like? How long have you known Richard? Why hasn't he married before? The mother, is she——'

'Lucy is a marvel in her way,' Gwen said.

'Oh, do you call her Lucy? You must know her awfully well.'

'I'm quite,' said Gwen, 'a member of the family in my way.'

'Richard has often told me that. Do you go there *every* Sunday?'

'Most Sundays,' Gwen said. 'It is often very amusing, and one sometimes sees a fresh face.'

'Why,' Trudy said, as the summer passed and she had already been away for several week-ends with Richard, 'doesn't he ask me to meet his mother? If my mother were alive and living in London I know I would have asked him home to meet her.'

Trudy threw out hints to Richard. 'How I wish you could meet my father. You simply must come up to Leicester in the Christmas holidays and stay with him.

He's rather tied up in Leicester and never leaves it. He's an insurance manager. The successful kind.'

'I can't very well leave Mother at Christmas,' Richard said, 'but I'd love to meet your father some other time.' His tan had worn off, and Trudy thought him more distinguished and at the same time more unattainable than ever.

'I think it only right,' Trudy said in her young young way, 'that one should introduce the man one loves to one's parents' — for it was agreed between them that they were in love.

But still, by the end of October, Richard had not asked her to meet his mother.

'Does it matter all that much?' Gwen said.

'Well, it would be a definite step forward,' Trudy said. 'We can't go on being just friends like this. I'd like to know where I stand with him. After all, we're in love and we're both free. Do you know, I'm beginning to think he hasn't any serious intentions after all. But if he asked me to meet his mother it would be a sort of sign, wouldn't it?'

'It certainly would,' Gwen said.

'I don't even feel I can ring him up at home until I've met his mother. I'd feel shy of talking to her on the phone. I must meet her. It's becoming a sort of obsession.'

'It certainly is,' Gwen said. 'Why don't you just say to him, "I'd like to meet your mother"?'

'Well, Gwen, there are some things a girl can't say.'

'No, but a woman can.'

'Are you going on about my age again? I tell you, Gwen, I feel twenty-two. I think twenty-two. I am twenty-two so far as Richard's concerned. I don't think really you can help me much. After all, you haven't been successful with men yourself, have you?'

'No,' Gwen said, 'I haven't. I've always been on the old side.'

'That's just my point. It doesn't get you anywhere to feel old and think old. If you want to be successful with men you have to hang on to your youth.'

'It wouldn't be worth it at the price,' Gwen said, 'to judge by the state you're in.'

Trudy started to cry and ran to her room, presently returning to ask Gwen questions about Richard's mother. She could rarely keep away from Gwen when she was not out with Richard.

'What's his mother really like? Do you think I'd get on with her?'

'If you wish I'll take you to see his mother one Sunday.'

'No, no,' Trudy said. 'It's got to come from him if it has any meaning. The invitation must come from Richard.'

Trudy had almost lost her confidence, and in fact had come to wonder if Richard was getting tired of her, since he had less and less time to spare for her, when unexpectedly and yet so inevitably, in November, he said, 'You must come and meet my mother.'

'Oh!' Trudy said.

'I should like you to meet my mother. She's looking forward to it.'

'Oh, does she know about me?'

'Rather.'

'Oh!'

'It's happened. Everything's all right,' Trudy said breathlessly.

'He has asked you home to meet his mother,' Gwen said without looking up from the exercise book she was correcting.

'It's important to me, Gwen.'

'Yes, yes,' Gwen said.

'I'm going on Sunday afternoon,' Trudy said. 'Will you be there?'

'Not till supper time,' Gwen said. 'Don't worry.'

'He said, "I want you to meet Mother. I've told her all about you."'

'All about you?'

'That's what he said, and it means so much to me, Gwen. So much.'

Gwen said, 'It's a beginning.'

'Oh, it's the beginning of everything. I'm sure of that.'

Richard picked her up in his Singer at four on Sunday. He seemed preoccupied. He did not, as usual, open the car door for her, but slid into the driver's seat and waited for her to get in beside him. She fancied he was perhaps nervous about her meeting his mother for the first time.

The house on Campion Hill was delightful. They must be very *comfortable*, Trudy thought. Mrs. Seeton was a tall, stooping woman, well dressed and preserved, with thick steel-grey hair and large light eyes. 'I hope you'll call me Lucy,' she said. 'Do you smoke?'

'I don't,' said Trudy.

'Helps the nerves,' said Mrs. Seeton, 'when one is getting on in life. You don't need to smoke yet awhile.'

'No,' Trudy said. 'What a lovely room, Mrs. Seeton.'

'*Lucy*,' said Mrs. Seeton.

'Lucy,' Trudy said, very shyly, and looked at

Richard for support. But he was drinking the last of his tea and looking out of the window as if to see whether the sky had cleared.

'Richard has to go out for supper,' Mrs. Seeton said, waving her cigarette holder very prettily. 'Don't forget to watch the time, Richard. But Trudy will stay to supper with me, I *hope*. Trudy and I have a lot to talk about, I'm sure.' She looked at Trudy and very faintly, with no more than a butterfly-flick, winked.

Trudy accepted the invitation with a conspiratorial nod and a slight squirm in her chair. She looked at Richard to see if he would say where he was going for supper, but he was gazing up at the top pane of the window, his fingers tapping on the arm of the shining Old Windsor chair on which he sat.

Richard left at half-past six, very much more cheerful in his going than he had been in his coming.

'Richard gets restless on a Sunday,' said his mother.

'Yes, so I've noticed,' Trudy said, so that there should be no mistake about who had been occupying his recent Sundays.

'I daresay now you want to hear all about Richard,' said his mother in a secretive whisper, although no one was in earshot. Mrs. Seeton giggled through her nose and raised her shoulders all the way up her long neck till they almost touched her ear-rings.

Trudy vaguely copied her gesture. 'Oh yes,' she said, 'Mrs. Seeton.'

'Lucy. You must call me Lucy, now, you know. I want you and me to be friends. I want you to feel like a member of the family. Would you like to see the house?'

She led the way upstairs and displayed her affluent bedroom, one wall of which was entirely covered by mirror, so that, for every photograph on her dressing table of Richard and Richard's late father, there were virtually two photographs in the room.

'This is Richard on his pony, Lob. He adored Lob. We all adored Lob. Of course, we were in the country then. This is Richard with Nana. And this is Richard's father at the outbreak of war. What did you do in the war, dear?'

'I was at school,' Trudy said, quite truthfully.

'Oh, then you're a teacher, too?'

'No, I'm a secretary. I didn't leave school till after the war.'

Mrs. Seeton said, looking at Trudy from two angles, 'Good gracious me, how deceiving. I thought you were about Richard's age, like Gwen. Gwen is such a dear. This is Richard as a graduate. Why he went into schoolmastering I don't know. Still, he's a very good master. Gwen always says so, quite definitely. Don't you adore Gwen?'

'Gwen is a good bit older than me,' Trudy said, being still upset on the subject of age.

'She ought to be here any moment. She usually comes for supper. Now I'll show you the other rooms and Richard's room.'

When they came to Richard's room his mother stood on the threshold and, with her finger to her lips for no apparent reason, swung the door open. Compared with the rest of the house this was a bleak, untidy, almost schoolboy's room. Richard's green pyjama trousers lay on the floor where he had stepped out of them. This was a sight familiar to Trudy from her several week-end excursions with Richard, of late months, to hotels up the Thames valley.

'So untidy,' said Richard's mother, shaking her head woefully. 'So untidy. One day, Trudy, dear, we must have a real chat.'

Gwen arrived presently, and made herself plainly at home by going straight into the kitchen to prepare a salad. Mrs. Seeton carved slices of cold meat while Trudy stood and watched them both, listening to a conversation between them which indicated a long intimacy. Richard's mother seemed anxious to please Gwen.

'Expecting Grace tonight?' Gwen said.

'No, darling, I thought perhaps not to*night*. Was I right?'

'Oh, of course, yes. Expecting Joanna?'

'Well, as it's Trudy's *first* visit, I thought perhaps not——'

'Would you,' Gwen said to Trudy, 'lay the table, my dear. Here are the knives and forks.'

Trudy bore these knives and forks into the dining-room with a sense of having been got rid of with a view to being talked about.

At supper, Mrs. Seeton said, 'It seems a bit odd, there only being the three of us. We usually have such jolly Sunday suppers. Next week, Trudy, you must come and meet the whole crowd — mustn't she, Gwen?'

'Oh yes,' Gwen said, 'Trudy must do that.'

Towards half-past ten Richard's mother said, 'I doubt if Richard will be back in time to run you home. Naughty boy, I daren't think what he gets up to.'

On the way to the bus stop Gwen said, 'Are you happy now that you've met Lucy?'

'Yes, I think so. But I think Richard might have

stayed. It would have been nice. I daresay he wanted me to get to know his mother by myself. But in fact I felt the need of his support.'

'Didn't you have a talk with Lucy?'

'Well yes, but not much really. Richard probably didn't realise you were coming to supper. Richard probably thought his mother and I could have a heart-to-heart——'

'I usually go to Lucy's on Sunday,' Gwen said.

'Why?'

'Well, she's a friend of mine. I know her ways. She amuses me.'

During the week Trudy saw Richard only once, for a quick drink.

'Exams,' he said. 'I'm rather busy, darling.'

'Exams in November? I thought they started in December.'

'Preparation for exams,' he said. 'Preliminaries. Lots of work.' He took her home, kissed her on the cheek and drove off.

She looked after the car, and for a moment hated his moustache. But she pulled herself together and, recalling her youthfulness, decided she was too young really to judge the fine shades and moods of a man like Richard.

He picked her up at four o'clock on Sunday.

'Mother's looking forward to seeing you,' he said. 'She hopes you will stay for supper.'

'You won't have to go out, will you, Richard?'

'Not tonight, no.'

But he did have to go out to keep an appointment of which his mother reminded him immediately after tea. He had smiled at his mother and said, 'Thanks.'

Trudy saw the photograph album, then she heard how Mrs. Seeton had met Richard's father in Switzerland, and what Mrs. Seeton had been wearing at the time.

At half-past six the supper party arrived. These were three women, including Gwen. The one called Grace was quite pretty, with a bewildered air. The one called Iris was well over forty and rather loud in her manner.

'Where's Richard tonight, the old cad?' said Iris.

'How do I know?' said his mother. 'Who am I to ask?'

'Well, at least he's a hard worker during the week. A brilliant teacher,' said doe-eyed Grace.

'Middling as a schoolmaster,' Gwen said.

'Oh, Gwen! Look how long he's held down the job,' his mother said.

'I should think,' Grace said, 'he's wonderful with the boys.'

'Those Shakespearean productions at the end of the summer term are really magnificent,' Iris bawled. 'I'll hand him that, the old devil.'

'Magnificent,' said his mother. 'You must admit, Gwen——'

'Very middling performances,' Gwen said.

'I suppose you are right, but, after all, they are only schoolboys. You can't do much with untrained actors, Gwen,' said Mrs. Seeton very sadly.

'I adore Richard,' Iris said, 'when he's in his busy, occupied mood. He's so——'

'Oh yes,' Grace said, 'Richard is wonderful when he's got a lot on his mind.'

'I know,' said his mother. 'There was one time when

Richard had just started teaching — I must tell you
this story — he . . .'

Before they left Mrs. Seeton said to Trudy, 'You
will come with Gwen next week, won't you? I want
you to regard yourself as one of us. There are two other
friends of Richard's I do want you to meet. Old
friends.'

On the way to the bus Trudy said to Gwen, 'Don't
you find it dull going to Mrs. Seeton's every Sunday?'

'Well, yes, my dear young thing, and no. From time
to time one sees a fresh face, and then it's quite amusing.'

'Doesn't Richard ever stay at home on a Sunday
evening?'

'No, I can't say he does. In fact, he's very often
away for the whole week-end. As you know.'

'Who are these women?' Trudy said, stopping in the
street.

'Oh, just old friends of Richard's.'

'Do they see him often?'

'Not now. They've become members of the family.'

The Fathers' Daughters

SHE left the old man in his deck-chair on the front, having first adjusted the umbrella awning with her own hand, and with her own hand, put his panama hat at a comfortable angle. The beach attendant had been sulky, but she didn't see why one should lay out tips only for adjusting an umbrella and a panama hat. Since the introduction of the new franc it was impossible to tip less than a franc. There seemed to be a conspiracy all along the coast to hide the lesser coins from the visitors, and one could only find franc pieces in one's purse, and one had to be careful not to embarrass Father, and one . . .

She hurried along the Rue Paradis, keeping in the hot shade, among all the old, old smells of Nice, not only garlic wafting from the cafés, and of the hot invisible air itself, but the smells from her memory, from thirty-five summers at Nice in apartments of long-ago, Father's summer salon, Father's friends' children, Father's friends, writers, young artists dating back five years at Nice, six, nine years; and then, before the war, twenty years ago — when we were at Nice, do you remember, Father? Do you remember the pension on the Boulevard Victor Hugo when we were rather poor? Do you remember the Americans at the Negresco in 1937 — how changed, how demure they are now!

Do you remember, Father, how in the old days we disliked the thick carpets — at least, you disliked them, and what you dislike, I dislike, isn't it so, Father?

Yes, Dora, we don't care for luxury. Comfort, yes, but luxury, no.

I doubt if we can afford to stay at an hotel on the front this year, Father.

What's that? What's that you say?

I said I doubt if we ought to stay on the front this year, Father; the Promenade des Anglais is becoming very trippery. Remember you disliked the thick carpets. . . .

Yes, yes, of course.

Of course, and so we'll go, I suggest, to a little place I've found on the Boulevard Gambetta, and if we don't like that there's a very good place on the Boulevard Victor Hugo. Within our means, Father, modest and . . .

What's that you say?

I said it wasn't a vulgar place, Father.

Ah. No.

And so I'll just drop them a note and book a couple of bedrooms. They may be small, but the food . . .

Facing the sea, Dora.

They are all very vulgar places facing the sea, Father. Very distracting. No peace at all. Times have changed, you know.

Ah. Well, I leave it to you, dear. Tell them I desire a large room, suitable for entertaining. Spare no expense, Dora.

Oh, of course not, Father.

And I hope to God we've won the lottery, she thought, as she hurried up the little street to the lottery kiosk. Someone's got to win it out of the whole of

France. The dark-skinned blonde at the lottery kiosk
took an interest in Dora who came so regularly each
morning rather than buy a newspaper to see the results.
She leaned over the ticket, holding her card of numbers,
comparing it with Dora's ticket, with an expression of
earnest sympathy.

'No luck,' Dora said.

'Try again tomorrow,' said the woman. 'One never
knows. Life is a lottery . . .'

Dora smiled as one who must either smile or weep.
On her way back to the sea-front she thought, tomorrow I will buy five hundred francs' worth. Then
she thought, no, no, I'd better not, I may run short of
francs and have to take Father home before time.
Dora, the food here is inferior. — I know, Father, but
it's the same everywhere in France now, times have
changed. — I think we should move to another hotel,
Dora. — The others are all very expensive, Father.
— What's that? What's that you say? — There are
no other rooms available, Father, because of the
tourists, these days.

The brown legs of lovely young men and girls passed
her as she approached the sea. I ought to appreciate
every minute of this, she thought, it may be the last
time. This thoroughly blue sea, these brown limbs,
these white teeth and innocent inane tongues, these
palm trees — all this is what we are paying for.

'Everything all right, Father?'

'Where have you been, dear?'

'Only for a walk round the back streets to smell the
savours.'

'Dora, you are a chip off the old block. What did
you see?'

'Brown limbs, white teeth, men in shirt sleeves behind café windows, playing cards with green bottles in front of them.'

'Good — you see everything with my eyes, Dora.'

'Heat, smell, brown legs — it's what we are paying for, Father.'

'Dora, you are becoming vulgar, if you don't mind my saying so. The eye of the true artist doesn't see life in the way of goods paid for. The world is ours. It is our birthright. We take it without payment.'

'I'm not an artist like you, Father. Let me move the umbrella — you mustn't get too much sun.'

'Times have changed,' he said, glancing along the pebble beach, 'the young men today have no interest in life.'

She knew what her father meant. All along the beach, the young men playing with the air, girls, the sun; they were coming in from the sea, shaking the water from their heads; they were walking over the pebbles, then splashing into the water; they were taking an interest in their environment with every pore of their skin, as Father would have said in younger days when he was writing his books. What he meant, now, when he said, 'the young men today have no interest in life' was that his young disciples, his admirers, had all gone, they were grown old and preoccupied, and had not been replaced. The last young man to seek out Father had been a bloodless-looking youth — not that one judged by appearances — who had called about seven years ago at their house in Essex. Father had made the most of him, giving up many of his mornings to sitting in the library talking about books with the young man, about life and the old days. But this, the last

of Father's disciples, had left after two weeks with a
promise to send them the article he was going to write
about Father and his works. Indeed he had sent a
letter: 'Dear Henry Castlemaine, — Words cannot
express my admiration . . .' After that they had heard
no more. Dora was not really sorry. He was a poor
specimen compared with the men who, in earlier days,
used to visit Father. Dora in her late teens could have
married one of three or four vigorous members of the
Henry Castlemaine set, but she had not done so because
of her widowed father and his needs as a public figure;
and now she sometimes felt it would have served Father
better if she had married, because of Father — one
could have contributed from a husband's income, perhaps, to his declining years.

Dora said, 'We must be going back to the hotel for
lunch.'

'Let us lunch somewhere else. The food there is . . .'

She helped her father from the deck chair and, turning to the sea, took a grateful breath of the warm blue
breeze. A young man, coming up from the sea, shook
his head blindly and splashed her with water; then
noticing what he had done he said — turning and
catching her by the arm — 'Oh, I'm so sorry.' He
spoke in English, was an Englishman, and she knew
already how unmistakably she was an Englishwoman.
'All right,' she said, with a quick little laugh. The
father was fumbling with his stick, the incident had
passed, was immediately forgotten by Dora as she took
his arm and propelled him across the wide hot boulevard where the white-suited policemen held up the
impetuous traffic. 'How would you like to be arrested
by one of those, Dora?' He gave his deep short laugh

and looked down at her. 'I'd love it, Father.' Perhaps he wouldn't insist on lunching elsewhere. If only they could reach the hotel, it would be all right; Father would be too exhausted to insist. But already he was saying, 'Let's find somewhere for lunch.'

'Well, we've paid for it at the hotel, Father.'

'Don't be vulgar, my love.'

In the following March, when Dora met Ben Donadieu for the first time, she had the feeling she had seen him somewhere before, she knew not where. Later, she told him of this, but he could not recall having seen her. But this sense of having seen him somewhere remained with Dora all her life. She came to believe she had met him in a former existence. In fact, it was on the beach at Nice that she had seen him, when he came up among the pebbles from the sea, and shook his hair, wetting her, and took her arm, apologising.

'Don't be vulgar, my love. The hotel food is appalling. Not French at all.'

'It's the same all over France, Father, these days.'

'There used to be a restaurant — what was its name? — in one of those little streets behind the Casino. Let's go there. All the writers go there.'

'Not any more, Father.'

'Well, so much the better. Let's go there in any case. What's the name of the place? — Anyway, come on, I could go there blindfold. All the writers used to go . . .'

She laughed, because, after all, he was sweet. As she walked with him towards the Casino she did not say — Not any more, Father, do the writers go there. The writers don't come to Nice, not those of moderate means. But there's one writer here this year, Father, called Kenneth Hope, whom you haven't heard about. He uses our beach, and I've seen him once — a shy, thin, middle-aged man. But he won't speak to anyone. He writes wonderfully, Father. I've read his novels, they open windows in the mind that have been bricked-up for a hundred years. I have read *The Inventors*, which made great fame and fortune for him. It is about the inventors of patent gadgets, what lives they lead, how their minds apply themselves to invention and to love, and you would think, while you were reading *The Inventors*, that the place they live in was dominated by inventors. He has that magic, Father — he can make you believe anything. Dora did not say this, for her father had done great work too, and deserved a revival. His name was revered, his books were not greatly spoken of, they were not read. He would not understand the fame of Kenneth Hope. Father's novels were about the individual consciences of men and women, no one could do the individual conscience like Father. 'Here we are, Father — this is the place, isn't it?'

'No, Dora, it's further along.'

'Oh, but that's the Tumbril; it's wildly expensive.'

'Really, darling!'

She decided to plead the heat, and to order only a slice of melon for lunch with a glass of her father's wine. Both tall and slim, they entered the restaurant. Her hair was drawn back, the bones of her face were good, her eyes were small and fixed ready for humour, for she had decided to be a spinster and do it properly; she looked forty-six and she did not look forty-six; her skin was dry; her mouth was thin, and was growing thinner with the worry about money. The father looked eighty years old, as he was. Thirty years ago people used to turn round and say, as he passed, 'That's Henry Castlemaine'.

Ben lay on his stomach on his mattress on the beach enclosure. Carmelita Hope lay on her mattress, next to him. They were eating rolls and cheese and drinking white wine which the beach attendant had brought to them from the café. Carmelita's tan was like a perfect garment, drawn skin-tight over her body. Since leaving school she had been in numerous jobs behind the scenes of film and television studios. Now she was out of a job again. She thought of marrying Ben, he was so entirely different from all the other men of her acquaintance, he was joyful and he was serious. He was also good-looking: he was half French, brought up in England. And an interesting age, thirty-one. He was a school teacher, but Father could probably get him a job in advertising or publishing. Father could do a lot of things for them both if only he would exert himself. Perhaps if she got married he would exert himself.

'Did you see your father at all yesterday, Carmelita?'

'No; as a matter of fact he's driven up the coast. I think he's gone to stay at some villa on the Italian border.'

'I should like to see more of him,' said Ben. 'And have a talk with him. I've never really had a chance to have a talk with him.'

'He's awfully shy,' said Carmelita, 'with my friends.'

Sometimes she felt a stab of dissatisfaction when Ben talked about her father. Ben had read all his books through and through — that seemed rather obsessive to Carmelita, reading books a second time and a third, as if one's memory was defective. It seemed to her that

Ben loved her only because she was Kenneth Hope's daughter, and then, again, it seemed to her that this couldn't be so, for Ben wasn't attracted by money and success. Carmelita knew lots of daughters of famous men, and they were beset by suitors who were keen on their fathers' money and success. But it was the books that Ben liked about her father.

'He never interferes with me,' she said. 'He's rather good that way.'

'I would like to have a long talk with him,' Ben said.

'What about? — He doesn't like talking about his work.'

'No, but a man like that. I would like to know his mind.'

'What about my mind?'

'You've got a lovely mind. Full of pleasant laziness. No guile.' He drew his forefinger from her knee to her ankle. She was wearing a pink bikini. She was very pretty and had hoped to become a starlet before her eighteenth birthday. Now she was very close to twenty-one and was thinking of marrying Ben instead, and was relieved that she no longer wanted to be an actress. He had lasted longer than any other boy friend. She had often found a boy exciting at first but usually went off him quite soon. Ben was an intellectual, and intellectuals, say what you like, seemed to last longer than anyone else. There was more in them to find out about. One was always discovering new things — she supposed it was Father's blood in her that drew her towards the cultivated type, like Ben.

He was staying at a tiny hotel in a back street near the old quay. The entrance was dark, but the room itself was right at the top of the house, with a little balcony. Carmelita was staying with friends at a villa. She spent a lot of time in Ben's room, and sometimes slept there. It was turning out to be a remarkably happy summer.

'You won't see much of Father,' she said, 'if we get married. He works and sees nobody. When he doesn't write he goes away. Perhaps he'll get married again and——'

'That's all right,' he said, 'I don't want to marry your father.'

Dora Castlemaine had several diplomas for elocution which she had never put to use. She got a part-time job, after the Christmas holidays that year, in Basil Street Grammar School in London, and her job was to try to reform the more pronounced Cockney accents of the more promising boys into a near-standard English. Her father was amazed.

'Money, money, you are always talking about money. Let us run up debts. One is nobody without debts.'

'One's credit is limited, Father. Don't be an old goose.'

'Have you consulted Waite?' Waite was the publisher's young man who looked after the Castlemaine royalties, diminishing year by year.

'We've drawn more than our due for the present.'

'Well, it's a bore, you going out to teach.'

'It may be a bore for you,' she said at last, 'but it isn't for me.'

'Dora, do you really mean you want to go to this job in London?'

'Yes, I want to. I'm looking forward to it.'

He didn't believe her. But he said, 'I suppose I'm a bit of a burden on you, Dora, these days. Perhaps I ought to go off and die.'

'Like Oates at the South Pole,' Dora commented.

He looked at her and she looked at him. They were shrewd in their love for each other.

She was the only woman teacher in the school, with hardly the status of a teacher. She had her own corner of the common room and, anxious to reassure the men that she had no intention of intruding upon them, would, during free periods, spread out on the table one of the weekly journals and study it intently, only looking up to say good morning or good afternoon to the masters who came in with piles of exercise books under their arms. Dora had no exercise books to correct, she was something apart, a reformer of vowel sounds. One of the masters, and then another, made conversation with her during morning break, when she passed round the sugar for the coffee. Some were in their early thirties. The ginger-moustached science master was not long graduated from Cambridge. Nobody said to her, as intelligent men had done as late as fifteen years ago, 'Are you any relation, Miss Castlemaine, to Henry Castlemaine the writer?'

Ben walked with Carmelita under the trees of Lincoln's Inn Fields in the spring of the year, after school, and watched the children at their games. They were a beautiful couple. Carmelita was doing secretarial work in the City. Her father was in Morocco, having first taken them out to dinner to celebrate their engagement.

Ben said, 'There's a woman at the school, teaching elocution.'

'Oh?' said Carmelita. She was jumpy, because since her father's departure for Morocco Ben had given a new turn to their relationship. He would not let her stay overnight in his flat in Bayswater, not even at the week-ends. He said it would be nice, perhaps, to practise restraint until they were married in the summer, and that would give them something to look forward to. 'And I'm interested to see,' said Ben, 'what we mean to each other without sex.'

This made her understand how greatly she had become obsessed with him. She thought perhaps he was practising a form of cruelty to intensify her obsession. In fact, he did want to see what they meant to each other without sex.

She called at his flat unexpectedly and found him reading, with piles of other books set out on the table as if waiting to be read.

She accused him: You only want to get rid of me so that you can read your books.

'The fourth form is reading Trollope,' he explained, pointing to a novel of Trollope's among the pile.

'But you aren't studying Trollope just now.'

He had been reading a life of James Joyce. He banged it down and said. 'I've been reading all my life, and you won't stop me, Carmelita.'

She sat down. 'I don't want to stop you,' she said.

'I know,' he said.

'We aren't getting on at all well without sex,' she said, and on that occasion stayed the night.

He was writing an essay on her father. She wished that her father had taken more interest in it. Father had taken them out to dinner with his party face, smiling and boyish. Carmelita had seen him otherwise — in his acute dejection, when he seemed hardly able to endure the light of day.

'What's the matter, Father?'

'There's a comedy of errors going on inside me, Carmelita.' He sat at his desk most of the day while he was in these moods, doing nothing. Then, during the night, he would perhaps start writing, and sleep all the next morning, and gradually in the following days the weight would pass.

'There's a man on the phone wants you, Father — an interview.'

'Tell him I'm in the Middle East.'

'What did you think of Ben, Father?'

'A terribly nice man, Carmelita. You've made the right choice, I think.'

'An intellectual — I do like them best, you know.'

'I'd say he was the student type. Always will be.'

'He wants to write an essay about you, Father. He's absolutely mad about your books.'

'Yes.'

'I mean, couldn't you help him, Father? Couldn't you talk to him about your work, you know?'

'Oh, God, Carmelita. It would be easier to write the bloody essay myself.'

'All right, all right. I was only asking.'

'I don't want any disciples, Carmelita. They give me the creeps.'

'Yes, yes, all right. I know you're an artist, Father, there's no need to show off your temperament. I only wanted you to help Ben. I only . . .'

I only, she thought as she walked in Lincoln's Inn

Fields with Ben, wanted him to help me. I should have
said, 'I want you to talk more to Ben, to help me.' And
Father would have said, 'How do you mean?' And I
would have said, 'I don't know, quite.' And he would
have said, 'Well, if you don't know what you mean,
how the hell do I?'

Ben was saying, 'There's a woman at the school,
teaching elocution.'

'Oh?' said Carmelita jumpily.

'A Miss Castlemaine. She's been there four months,
and I only found out today that she's the daughter of
Henry Castlemaine.'

'But he's dead!' said Carmelita.

'Well, I thought so, too. But apparently he isn't
dead, he's very much alive in a house in Essex.'

'How old is Miss Castlemaine?' said Carmelita.

'Middle-aged. Middle forties. Perhaps late forties.
She's a nice woman, a classic English spinster. She
teaches the boys to say "How now brown cow". You
could imagine her doing wood engravings in the Cots-
wolds. I only found out today——'

'You might manage to get invited to meet him, with
any luck,' Carmelita said.

'Yes, she said I must come and see him, perhaps for
a weekend. Miss Castlemaine is going to arrange it.
She was awfully friendly when she found I was a Castlemaine admirer. A lot of people must think he's dead.
Of course, his work belongs to a past world, but it's
wonderful. Do you know *The Pebbled Shore*? — that's
an early one.'

'No, but I've read *Sin of Substance*, I think. It——'

'You mean *The Sinner and the Substance*. Oh, it has
fine things in it. Castlemaine's due for a revival.'

Carmelita felt a sharp stab of anger with her father, and then a kind of despair which was not as yet entirely familiar to her, although already she wondered if this was how Father felt in his great depressions when he sat all day, staring and enduring, and all night miraculously wrote the ache out of his system in prose of harsh merriment.

Helplessly, she said, 'Castlemaine's novels aren't as good as Father's, are they?'

'Oh, there's no comparison. Castlemaine is quite different. You can't say one type is *better* than another — goodness me!' He was looking academically towards the chimney stacks of Lincoln's Inn. This was the look in which she loved him most. After all, she thought, the Castlemaines might make everything easier for both of us.

'Father, it's really rather absurd. A difference of sixteen years. . . . People will say——'

'Don't be vulgar, Dora dear. What does it matter what people say? Mere age makes no difference when there's a true affinity, a marriage of true minds.'

'Ben and I have a lot in common.'

'I know it,' he said, and sat a little higher in his chair.

'I shall be able to give up my job, Father, and spend my time here with you again. I never really wanted that job. And you are so much in better health now . . .'

'I know.'

'And Ben will be here in the evenings and the weekends. You get on well with Ben, don't you?'

'A remarkably fine man, Dora. He'll go far. He's perceptive.'

'He's keen to revive your work.'

'I know. He should give up that job, as I told him, and devote himself entirely to literary studies. A born essayist.'

'Oh, Father, he'll have to keep his job for the meantime, anyhow. We'll need the money. It will help us all; we——'

'What's that? What's that you say?'

'I said he finds work in the grammar school stimulating, Father.'

'Do you love the man?'

'It's a little difficult to say, at my age, Father.'

'To me, you both seem children. Do you love him?'

'I feel,' she said, 'that I have known him much longer than I have. Sometimes I think I've known him all my life. I'm sure we have met before, perhaps even in a former existence. That's the decisive factor. There's something of *destiny* about my marrying Ben; do you know what I mean?'

'Yes, I think I do.'

'He was engaged, last year for a short time, to marry quite a young girl,' she said. 'The daughter of a novelist called Kenneth Hope. Have you heard of him, Father?'

'Vaguely,' he said. 'Ben,' he said, 'is a born disciple.'

She looked at him and he looked at her, shrewd in their love for each other.

The Party Through the Wall

Narrator. (*Dr. Fell.*) Most of the houses in Romney Terrace are bomb damage, they lie open to the Kensington weather like the decayed hollow teeth of some prone — or do I mean supine? — monster. Two of the houses at the end of the Terrace have been repaired and made over into flats. Some months ago, Miss Ethel Carson came to live in the last but one, number ten, on the third floor. I myself live next door in number eleven.

You will wonder how it is that I, with my secluded habits, came to know so much about Miss Carson. But, as you will see, I had unique opportunities to study this lady, even before she told me all about herself.

One of the first things Miss Carson asked the housekeeper when she came to look over the flat was a question which she always asked in these circumstances.

Miss Carson. Is it quiet?

Housekeeper. Too quiet, miss. Too quiet.

Miss Carson. It can't be too quiet for me. No wirelesses? No babies? I sleep badly. I suffer from my nerves. No late parties in the house?

Housekeeper. No, no parties, miss.

Miss Carson. It looks rather small. Is it damp?

Housekeeper. No, miss, no damp. See for yourself, miss.

Miss Carson. Don't call me miss, it gets on my nerves. My name is Miss Carson, Ethel Carson — you won't have heard of me but I am known in certain circles. Where's the bedroom? Is it facing the back? It has to face the back of the house. I can't stand traffic. I suffer from sleeplessness.

Housekeeper. In here. It looks out on the back.

Miss Carson. It's rather small. Who lives on the other side of the wall?

Housekeeper. That's number eleven. All made over into flats.

Miss Carson. The wall is very thin. Are they noisy at number eleven? Shall I hear them at night having parties or quarrelling and screaming? Do they have the wireless on late at night? The wall is rather thin.

Housekeeper. It's a quiet place. Ideal for anyone that's getting on in life.

Miss Carson. It must be ideal for *you*. Tell me, do you think it odd that I am wearing these clothes at my age? Where's the kitchen? Does it smell?

Housekeeper. Do you want the flat? There's another party after it.

Miss Carson. Oh, must I make up my mind right away? How disturbing.

Housekeeper. There's another party wants it that's out all day.

Narrator. Miss Carson took the flat and moved in the following week. I believe she was generally satisfied, though, in the first month of her stay, I understand there was some trouble about mice.

Miss Carson. Mice in my kitchen. I am a vegetarian, which attracts mice. I mean the cheese, I use a lot of cheese. I cannot have mice.

Housekeeper. I'll set a trap, miss.

Miss Carson. No, no. I should be unable to sleep at night because of the squeaking of mice in the trap. And don't call me miss, it gets on my nerves.

Housekeeper. I'll put a cat in the kitchen at night, then.

Miss Carson. Oh, I call that very cruel. I couldn't bear it. How disturbing.

Narrator. Eventually the mice were eliminated by means of a powdered preparation which killed them silently and without evidence.

For at least three months I watched Miss Carson's comings and goings, and noted her special times and habits. Really I conceived an interest in her. Of course, it was a detached interest, as becomes my position in life.

I observed that, for a woman in her fifties, she looked, I will not say young, but neat and unusual. She must have been a little unusual from the time of her youth.

Miss Carson. I have been an unusual person from the time of my youth. My earliest memories——

Housekeeper. I can see that, miss.

Narrator. And as a rule, when Miss Carson emerged from the front door of number ten she was wearing a snow-white duffle coat over pink velvet corduroy jeans. She kept her hair a pale yellow, drawn straight back so that its thinness was concealed. Her rimless glasses added to the pastel effect. She was most quaint. I could see she was an exceptional, a very exceptional case.

One day, at last, when no one was about, I spoke to her. Ever since my retirement I have tried to keep in the background, and to some extent I avoid company. But as we were alone in the street, about three in the afternoon, I spoke. 'Good afternoon, madam,' I said. 'Nice day.'

Miss Carson. I beg your pardon?

Narrator. I said, beautiful day.

Miss Carson. Oh, I suppose it is.

Narrator. Allow me to introduce myself. I am your next-door neighbour, as it were. I believe you have not been here long?

Miss Carson. No, I suppose I haven't.

Narrator. I am the proprietor of number eleven. My name is Fell.

Miss Carson. Good afternoon, Mr. Fell. I am in rather a hurry, if you don't mind.

Narrator. Doctor Fell, madam. A man of medicine.

Miss Carson. Indeed, that is interesting. Do you practise?

Narrator. If you are in a hurry, madam, perhaps another time.

Miss Carson. Do you practise here, Dr. Fell? I'm in no great hurry.

Narrator. Rarely, madam, in these days. Unless I find an exceptionally interesting case. I am a specialist, and an exceptional case is a very great temptation, very great, madam.

Miss Carson. You keep calling me madam; I must tell you it jars on my nerves. My name is Ethel Carson. You won't have heard of me, but I am known in certain circles. What do you specialise in, Dr. Fell?

Narrator. Nerves, madam. I specialise in nerves. But only exceptional cases — they are irresistible.

Miss Carson. Now that *is* fascinating. We must have some talks together, Dr. Fell.

Narrator. For some months Miss Carson was satisfied with the quietness of Romney Terrace. A street which is nearly all bomb damage is always quiet. We have no traffic. Not many rough children play here by day, not many stray cats come here at night. Numbers ten and eleven are occupied by people of silent habits — Miss Carson, how about the housekeeper?

Miss Carson. Oh, she's quiet enough. Of course, she is sly. But she is quiet. I should explain that I lead a sequestered though busy life. I am devoted to art and to all spiritual matters: I should rather say, dedicated.

Narrator. The dedicated life takes up an enormous amount of Miss Carson's time. And also, she has to look after her investments which take up an enormous amount of time. As Miss Carson says, she can't leave these matters to others.

In the mornings she has her bath, does her deep breathing, and meditates. On Monday afternoons she goes to the hairdresser, and from there to her physio-therapist who is also a masseuse.

Miss Carson. Dr. Fell, do you believe in the occult?

Narrator. One thing at a time, madam, if you please . . . To continue with Miss Carson's daily round. Some-times she meets her young friends while she is out and about. Most of her friends are young. She doesn't care for old fogies. That's why I, who am getting on, am favoured in having cultivated Miss Carson's acquaintance.

Miss Carson. I wish you would call me Ethel, Dr. Fell. Miss Carson gets dreadfully on my nerves. All my friends call me Ethel. All my friends are young, except you, and sensitive to the spiritual life, like you.

Narrator. Thank you, Ethel.

On Tuesdays, Miss Carson attends to her business affairs, and in that way she has come across a number of interesting speculators.

Miss Carson. You would be surprised how sensitive some City men are to spiritual matters. . . .

Narrator. To continue with Miss Carson's daily round. Tuesday evening is her night for the Kensington Cabbalah Study Group of which she is an active member. Wednesdays, if her nerves permit, she spends on her automatic writing.

Miss Carson. Oh, Dr. Fell, have you ever experimented with automatic writing? Of course, in this rationalistic age it has gone out of fashion, but it will come back, like all those things. The great thing in life is to keep an open mind. By the way, Dr. Fell, have you ever had that extraordinary feeling that everything has happened before?

Narrator. Ethel, I must ask you to exercise patience. How can I tell the story when you keep interrupting?

Miss Carson. Rightee-o.

Narrator. I must request you, Ethel, not to say 'rightee-o'. It gets on my nerves.

Miss Carson. I don't think a professional man should use an expression like 'gets on my nerves'. It is rather low, in my opinion.

Narrator. (*Over above.*) On Wednesdays her young friend David, who is a ballet dancer, comes to spend a few hours with Miss Carson.

Miss Carson. He is very sensitive and according to his horoscope his future is assured. He is . . .

Narrator. Miss Carson has explained what she does on Mondays, Tuesdays and Wednesdays. Well, Thursdays, Fridays, Saturdays and Sundays are much the same. She has her Dream Prognostication Circle and her Astral-Radiation Trance Club. She meditates much. And a great deal of her time is taken up in preparing her vegetarian meals.

Miss Carson. So many people neglect the roots and fruits of the earth; how they survive I can't think. And then, of course, I frequently spend a little time chatting to Dr. Fell, who, I must admit, is sensitive to the life of the spirit.

Narrator. Thank you, Ethel. I would invite you to tea, but I am prevented from entertaining because of my poor sister.

Miss Carson. I didn't know you had a sister. Is she ill? Is she bed-ridden? I can't stand illness, it gets on my . . . it does dreadful things to my nerves.

Narrator. She is confined to her room. She is as quiet as the grave.

Miss Carson. I sympathise with you, Dr. Fell. Invalids are a great trial.

Narrator. That was six weeks ago. Miss Carson has now left Romney Terrace, isn't that so, Ethel? ... You see, no answer. She's gone. Now I shall tell you why she left Romney Terrace.

Some days before she departed I saw Miss Carson coming out of number ten a little earlier than usual. She looked very put out that morning, and instead of turning up the street she stood out in the middle of the road and stared up at the windows of number eleven. I thought I had better put in an appearance. I said, 'Good morning, Ethel. Is anything the matter?'

Miss Carson. I should think there is, Dr. Fell. I couldn't sleep a wink last night, on account of the dreadful noise.

Narrator. Noise, did you say? In Romney Terrace?

Miss Carson. The noise came from your house, Dr. Fell. It was a party.

Narrator. A party at number eleven? But we never have parties, on account of my poor sister.

Miss Carson. I insist that someone in your house held a party late last night. It was in the room next to my bedroom, on the third floor.

Narrator. That is my poor sister's room, Ethel. She is quiet as the grave.

Miss Carson. She must have been giving a party. It was frightful. It lasted till four in the morning. I was just coming to call on you to complain in the strongest terms.

Narrator. I was convinced that poor Miss Carson was suffering from her nerves. You see, she acted like a magnet upon me. You see, she called out the compulsive instinct of the specialist in me. I could not leave her alone, she was an extraordinary case. Indeed, she would not leave me alone, she was determined to complain of the noise.

Miss Carson. There was a great hubbub, Dr. Fell. Music and chatter. I had gone to bed about eleven o'clock, having just said goodbye to my young friend, David, the ballet dancer. I was rather worried about David because *he* was worried, and this was because one of his companions at the ballet school and that was because . . . (*Fade.*)

Narrator. Yes, yes . . . She took her phenobarbitone as usual. But she could not sleep. She lay awake worrying. . . .

Miss Carson. I lay awake till it must have been close on three in the morning.

Narrator. Observe that up to this point not even a clock ticked. Miss Carson has an electric clock to avoid the tick. Her bed is placed with the head against the wall which separates her flat from my sister's in number eleven.

Miss Carson. I had never before experienced trouble from number eleven, not a sound. But now, as I lay worrying, awake, I suddenly thought I heard a noise. Was it my imagination, or could that be the playing of a piano in the room through the wall? It wasn't my imagination, Dr. Fell.

(*Piano playing and party chatter*)

Voice 1. (*Over.*) How beautifully you play, Countess. What are you playing? It is difficult to follow through this hullabaloo.

Countess. (*Young — in her twenties.*) Liszt — I was present at a party in London when he played, not long before his death. Do you think I should stop? Everyone is so noisy and occupied. They don't want music.

Voice 1. Don't stop, Countess, it's heavenly. How I do wish I were a widow!

(*Piano stops*)

Countess. A widow! How comical you are, and you're not even married yet.

Voice 1. I wish to be a widow, rather. I would cultivate musicians, I would . . .

(*Noise as of banging on wall with a shoe. Chatter down.*)

Miss Carson. Stop that noise! I can't sleep.

(*More banging on wall with shoe. Chatter*)

Voice 3.	Goodbye then, Countess. A delightful evening . . .
Voice 2.	You played beautifully. What was that last piece? Weber?
Voice 3.	Meyerbeer . . .
Voice 2.	Oh, Meyerbeer, of course, of course . . .
Voice 3.	Ta-ta, Countess, as they say . . .
Voice 4.	Margaret dear, stand out of that draught; your kidneys . . .
Voice 5.	. . . brought home a polar bear; of course it died . . . Countess, lovely party . . .

(*More banging on wall with shoe*)

Miss Carson. Stop that noise! I can't sleep.

(*Party chatter continues under above*)

Voice 6. Such a relief for you, Countess, now that your brother is away, I'm sure.

Countess. He isn't away, you know.

Voice 6. Not away, Countess? I heard to the contrary.

Countess. He is here, but out of sight.

Voice 6. Surely, my dear, he is not in this house?

Countess. Dear friend, can you keep a secret? My brother is in the attic.

Voice 6. The attic! Is he safe?

Countess. Altogether safe. We have made it very comfortable.

Voice 6. I mean is it safe for you? Has he a keeper?

Countess. He has an attendant.

Voice 1.	Goodbye then, Countess. Charming party.
Countess.	Goodbye, good night.
Voice 2.	Tomorrow at five, Countess?
Countess.	Tomorrow? Oh, that depends . . .
Voice 3.	Ta-ta . . .
Servant.	The carriages are waiting, sir.
Countess.	Take care, it's turning cold. Good night.
Voice 4.	The carriages. What a night!

Miss Carson. (*Shouting from window.*) Oh, go away home and stop that hell of a row. I want to sleep.

Narrator. Ethel, I think, if I may say so, you are suffering from nerves.

Miss Carson. *I* should say I am suffering from my nerves after a night like that. You must give your tenant notice to quit, Dr. Fell. I shall see my lawyer. It is an offence.

Narrator. Now, consider. You say that the guests were taken home in carriages. Is that likely? Is it reasonable? We are in the second half of the twentieth century, and you talk of carriages.

Miss Carson. I *saw* the carriages, Dr. Fell. A fancy-dress stunt, I daresay. Who occupies the room next to mine? Who is your tenant?

Narrator. My poor sister occupies that room. She is very feeble and quite incapable of parties.

Miss Carson. Her name?

Narrator. Oh, one calls her the Countess.

Miss Carson. I insist on seeing your sister. I want to get to the bottom of this.

Narrator. Cases like Miss Carson always want to get to the bottom of things, and when they get there, they don't like it. Follow me, Ethel, and I shall take you to my sister, so old and quiet, confined to her room.

(*Their footsteps*)

Miss Carson. Oh, the passage is very dark. I can't see my way, Dr. Fell.

Narrator. We ought to have a light, but the bulb has gone. The ground-floor tenant should see to it, but he is seldom at home. Follow me closely; my sister is on the third floor.

Miss Carson. In the room adjacent to my bedroom?

Narrator. Exactly adjacent, Ethel.

Miss Carson. I would rather you did not call me Ethel. I must get to the bottom of this, you realise.

Narrator. When I had introduced Miss Carson to the Countess, I made myself scarce, so to speak. My sister does not always care for my presence.

Countess. (*Aged.*) Is my brother in the room? My eyes are weak. I do not at all care for his presence.

Miss Carson. No, Countess, Dr. Fell is not here.

Countess. Dr. Fell my eye.

Miss Carson. I beg your pardon?

Countess. I said, Dr. Fell my eye. My brother is a madman. What is your business? State your business.

Miss Carson. I live next door in number ten. My flat is on the third floor, on the other side of that wall which you are facing.

Countess. Return to it.

Miss Carson. What?

Countess. Your flat. Kindly return to it.

Miss Carson. I have come to complain. I was kept awake all last night by your guests. They were making a frightful noise. If it occurs again I shall see my solicitor and call the police.

Countess. Madam, I have not entertained for fifty years. Observe the dust.

Miss Carson. Dust everywhere, and such a lot of furniture. It is most peculiar.

Countess. So are you.

Miss Carson. What?

Countess. Most peculiar. This is a lumber room and I am part of the lumber.

Miss Carson. There was a Countess playing the piano and she had locked her brother in the attic. I won't have it. My nerves are not strong.

Countess. Madam, if I unwind myself from these shawls and rugs you will see my face, and your nerves will be less strong. Look at my hands, like claws. They have not touched a piano for half a century. Come, take my hand and feel it.

Miss Carson. Oh no, I'd rather not. I must go, I must.

Countess. Will you come again?

Miss Carson. I shall speak to Dr. Fell.

Countess. Because, if you come again, I shall see my lawyer and call the police. Your attire is most peculiar.

Miss Carson. I shall speak to Dr. Fell.

Countess. Dr. Fell my eye.

Narrator. You see, Ethel, the trouble is that your nerves are very bad. You are a most interesting case. I specialise in nerves, and a particular type of nerves. I have diagnosed your case. You are quite my type of case. I have formed a theory.

Miss Carson. I shall get to the bottom of this, Dr. Fell.

Narrator. I shall help you to get to the bottom of it. My consulting room is upstairs. Follow me. You are an irresistible case, Ethel.

Miss Carson. I am aware that I am an interesting case. My friends at the Dream Prognostication Circle and the members of the Astral-Radiation Trance Club all tell me so, Dr. Fell.

Narrator. This way, Ethel. I live at the very top of the house.

Miss Carson. Oh, this is the attic! I wish to leave the house. Where's the front door?

Narrator. I thought you wanted to get to the bottom of things. Sit down and calm yourself. What did you think of my sister?

Miss Carson. Most objectionable. Quite unnatural, sitting alone amongst all that lumber. I shall definitely see my lawyer.

Narrator. That room was once the drawing-room in this house. My sister preferred it to those on the lower floor, it gave so much more light. She used to entertain on a magnificent scale. Those times are past. But my sister broods a great deal. I daresay you observed that she is a little, shall we say, odd, weak in the head?

Miss Carson. I did. I was not told of it when I took my flat. I shall complain to my housekeeper. I can't be kept awake at nights by a disorderly neighbour who is wrong in the head. I call this a most unpleasant situation.

Narrator. While Miss Carson was talking I could see she was looking round my attic taking in everything like a greedy busybody. I suppose she thought the pictures on the wall very odd. They are very strange. Poor Miss Carson, after her sleepless night and her encounter with my sister, was in a rather jumpy state.

Miss Carson. I am in a rather jumpy state. Can't you do something about it, as you're a specialist in nerves?

Narrator. That's the very idea, Ethel. I can assist you with your nerves. This brings me to my theory. I specialise, Ethel, in a particular type of mentality which is exactly your type.

Miss Carson. Oh, what type is that?

Narrator. One which we might call *haunted*. Ethel, in common parlance you are being haunted. I specialise in hauntings. You must let me treat you. Place your confidence in me. I have the experience. I am sensitive to the spiritual life around us.

Miss Carson. Do you mean that I imagined the noise last night? Because if that's what you mean . . .

Narrator. *Imagined!* Let us not be crude, I don't speak of imagination, but of a rare acuteness of the senses, an extreme sensitivity to the life of the invisible world. Ethel, you are an exciting case.

Miss Carson. You are very perceptive, Dr. Fell. What is your theory?

Narrator. My theory is this. There, on the third floor, my old sister, the Countess, sits brooding on the past before she lost her fortune and her wits. She relives the past, returning fifty years to the time when she was a young woman, talented and beautiful, with a distinguished reputation. Now, by means of telepathy——

Miss Carson. Telepathy!

Narrator. — My sister's mind has been conveyed to yours, so that what you heard last night was an emanation, Ethel, from my poor sister. I need not remind you, Ethel, that you are a unique case, in that you are particularly alive to the invisible forces around us. So am I. However, the fact remains that you have been haunted by the living thoughts of my sister. It is quite simple. I shall give you a course of analytic treatment and you will be haunted no more.

Miss Carson. I shall find another flat. I cannot continue to live in the next flat to that woman. I refuse to be haunted.

Narrator. You may be equally haunted elsewhere, Ethel.

Miss Carson. Don't call me Ethel. It all sounds a lot of rot to me.

Narrator. That is no way for a leading member of the Astral-Radiation Trance Club to talk, Ethel. Place your confidence in me. Now, I shall expect you to call on me at eleven tomorrow morning to report any unusual event which may have occurred during the night. I shall make no charge. I don't pretend to be disinterested, I am profoundly drawn towards a case of your kind.

Miss Carson. Oh, my nerves will never stand it! I am exhausted already.

Narrator. Leave your nerves to me, Ethel. Leave them to me.

Miss Carson. I went to bed that night at half-past ten. My nerves were so exhausted, I fell asleep immediately.

(Piano)

About three in the morning I was awakened by a piano playing. It sounded perfectly clear, and I was quite sure that it came from the room of that frightful Countess. I sat up in bed and switched on the light, trying to keep myself as collected as possible.

Narrator. (*Slightly hoarse.*) My sister, where's my sister? Ah, there you are. Why have you stopped playing?

Countess. What are you doing out of bed? Where is your attendant — what is he thinking of? Oh, don't glare at me in that terrible way. Keep calm. Follow me. Come upstairs with me.

Narrator. Why have you stopped playing? Do I frighten you?

Countess. Let me out of this room! Come away from that door and let me go! Where is your attendant?

Narrator. My keeper is upstairs in my attic. In my bed. With his throat cut.

Countess. (*Screams.*)

Narrator. Stop screaming, my dear, stop screaming. Stop, stop, stop. That's better. Now you've stopped screaming, haven't you? (*Laughing.*)

Miss Carson. I took a couple of phenobarbitones at dawn, and slept late into the morning. Then I rose and dressed and went downstairs to speak to the housekeeper.

Housekeeper. Did you call me, miss?

Miss Carson. I shall have to leave this house.

Housekeeper. I should, miss.

Miss Carson. I have to complain about a frightful noise.

Housekeeper. I did hear you, miss. You give a scream. I suppose it was nightmares, miss.

Miss Carson. Don't call me miss, it shatters my nerves. I have to complain about the house next door. It is disorderly. The people are irresponsible. I shall see my lawyer and inform the police.

Housekeeper. Number eleven, miss? They are all very quiet and respectable people there. Too quiet. No gramophones, no wirelesses, no babies. It belongs to a private company that won't have anyone in the house except old retired parties.

Miss Carson. You are misinformed. It belongs to a Dr. Fell. He has been deliberately causing a disturbance these past two nights. I shall give him in charge.

Housekeeper. I shouldn't do anything to provoke anyone, miss.

Narrator. My scientific curiosity mounted as Miss Carson came up the front-door steps of our house at eleven o'clock that morning.

(*Bell*)

She seemed very incensed — didn't you, Ethel?

(*Bell*)

Why did you ring the bell in that frantic fashion?

(*Door opens*)

Miss Carson. Oh, who opened the door?

Narrator. You see, Miss Carson was surprised — weren't you, Ethel? — when the door opened apparently by itself.

Miss Carson. Dr. Fell, come downstairs at once! I have had enough of your irresponsible tricks; I wish to speak to you.

Narrator. I am downstairs. I am standing beside you. I'm glad to see you have come promptly for your treatment.

Miss Carson. I can't see you. Where are you? I hear your voice, Dr. Fell, but I can't see you. It is disgraceful, a nerve specialist upsetting a woman's nerves. You will be sued for heavy damages. You will be

247

struck off the medical register. Come out of hiding and face me!

Narrator. Well, I didn't care to face her on that occasion. Why should I? The treatment was free. And, as I explained to Miss Carson, I have nothing to lose. I'm dead. So is my sister. I strangled her, as a matter of fact. (Didn't I, Ethel? — you heard the screams last night. That was a good fifty years ago.)

Now, won't you come up to my attic, Ethel, and we shall get to the bottom of this. Come to the attic and we shall continue with your nerve treatment. Don't mind my being invisible.

Miss Carson. I'm being haunted! I shall see my solicitor! I shall call the police! I am haunted!

Narrator. Precisely my diagnosis, you must admit. I specialise in hauntings, I am sensitive to the life of the spirit around us. (*Pause.*)

Miss Carson has left number ten. Just as well, she was getting frightfully on my nerves, she gave me the creeps. Didn't you, Ethel? Didn't you give me the creeps? Didn't you get on my nerves?

THE END

PRINTED BY PURNELL AND SONS, LTD.
PAULTON (SOMERSET) AND LONDON